THE 7 *TYPES* OF DOCTORS

AMIT MEHTA, M.D.

D1453086

AUTHOR'S NOTE

*To my wife, Khushbu, and children
without whose unwavering enthusiasm and support
this book would not be possible*

*Wherever the art of medicine is loved,
there is also a love of humanity.*

—Hippocrates

THE 7 TYPES OF DOCTORS

CONTENTS

INTRODUCTION

T he first day of internship training for a doctor is a quintessentially momentous day. It crystallizes that transformative moment when you are no longer a "student doctor" or "the medical student" or simply the most junior member of the troops of medical teams tending to patients through the hospital. It is also quite obviously a visually apparent step as well: this day is traditionally when one finally dons a long white coat (knee length), which is a proud step up the food chain from the short white coat (waist length) of a medical student. At long last, you are a medical doctor, with the golden M.D. embroidered after your name on your bright new white coat.

For many freshly graduated doctors, it is also an occasion of relief and reflection. After all, one cannot pass medical school without having endured years of examinations along with grueling days and nights of studying. I could not help but think of the great bonds my friends and I had formed after these years of sharing a common journey. Though we all were cognizant of the date of graduation, and the start of internship, it was still surreal when it finally hit me that my classmates and I had officially joined that prestigious club of medical doctors. It is a timeless profession, for as long as *Homo sapiens* has roamed the Earth, people have suffered physical ailments and sought healing. And now, between graduation and officially starting our training, we were happily immersed in graduation parties, surrounded by proud parents and families, and hanging out with our good friends before the real work of *doctoring* was about to begin.

During medical school, we were steeped in what a doctor should aspire to be and how to act. Sometimes these lessons were conveyed directly, such as when we collectively undertook the Hippocratic oath, reciting it at the beginning of our first year. Other times this was by implication, when in the midst of a professor demonstrating how to interview a patient, I felt we had to emulate not merely the words but some of the mannerisms, seating position, tone of voice, and inflections also. There were also instances when this was instilled by the annals of medical history. This was in the form of articles published in the scientific literature, including in prominent journals such as *The New England Journal of Medicine*, as well as required coursework such as the first-year class "Introduction to the Patient." I sensed this was also literally embodied by the immense alabaster statue of Hippocrates, the legendary physician from ancient Greece, standing tall in the gardens along the path to the main entrance to the school.

As that first day of internship rapidly approached, when we would be working with the newly anointed title of M.D., the excitement was building. I vividly recall trekking to a shop a few blocks from the hospital on a hot day in late June, where I picked up three new white coats with my name on them in blue thread. Later that evening, I relaxed at a casual dinner at a local restaurant, getting pizza with my parents, now only a weekend away from internship's kickoff. It did not strike me then, but with all of the focus on human anatomy, pathophysiology, pharmacology, and even medical history, we had barely touched what real-world medical practice was like. Filing appeals with health insurance companies, combating patient out-of-pocket costs, job stress, and burnout were decidedly not part of the medical curriculum.

Traditionally medical training follows the academic calendar, and so it was for me, on July 1st, when I was an intern assigned to one of the most demanding units in the hospital, the medical intensive care unit (MICU). This is where the most unstable patients are admitted. Many patients are on mechanical ventilators, colloquially referred to as breathing machines, others with life threatening infections, and then there are those patients who may have suffered a major heart attack. I arrived at the hospital around 6:15 a.m. that morning and reached the MICU by 6:30 a.m. This was not only the time when work started but also when you would hear the report of the updates of the patients from the previous night. There is always one team—comprised of a senior resident and an intern—that would remain in the hospital on-call overnight. This would be in the midst of a 30-hour shift for the two doctors assigned to that night. When I trained, these periodic extended shifts were both the norm and a rite of passage but nowadays are not allowed, intriguingly to the *detriment* of patients and medical education. More on that later.

There was added significance that morning for the doctors on-call updating my senior resident and I, being that the previous night was June 30. For on this day, now July 1, the intern who worked the overnight shift had officially become a second-year resident. I still remember my colleague's beaming expression when he completed his report of the events from the night. He was unquestionably happy; he had survived his harrowing intern year of countless critical medical scenarios, learning how to balance the workload while remaining thorough and combing medical journals and textbooks to promptly diagnose and treat his patients. In sum, he had become leaps and bounds wiser in the ways of doctoring over the past year since med school graduation. My senior resident (a third-year) gave him a congratulatory pat on the shoulder as well.

We had an upbeat feeling as we saw our multiple critical patients on the ward. I can liken it to the first day of high school or college and the associated excitement of the newness of the moment. My senior resident pointed to the schedule as we exited the conference room on the floor, that rounds would start at 8:30 a.m. with the attending physician. The attending is the head doctor and also our professor for that month on that rotation. While technically, from a legal perspective, the attending is the doctor in charge, our professor is also relying on the trainees to assiduously care for every patient and attend to every detail. After all, in the intensive care unit, patients can die and unfortunately some will. It is unfathomable that even the sharpest doctor could handle all of the 40-something MICU patients himself. And sharp he was, as my senior resident stated, so we better be prepared for patient rounds.

At 8:25 a.m., all of the interns and residents gathered in the conference room, awaiting the attending physician's presence. He came in within a minute and greeted all of us cordially. He was a tall individual, well-spoken, and had a deserved reputation as being very intelligent but also practical. After all, in the life-and-death world of the MICU, while we all had good camaraderie, it was still all business. Within moments we walked out en masse to one end of the ward, near the first patient's room.

This was it. I'll never forget that moment—the commencement of rounds on July 1 of intern year. I even recall the collective sound of the boots as we walked down the hall. We had spent the last two hours seeing our patients, but somehow this moment with the attending physician washed over me with the sense of "this is real." With all of the studying and examinations behind us, we as interns were truly assuming the mantle of being a physician.

Rounds were grueling that first week. There was a precipitously steep learning curve, far beyond what you were able to extract from your clinical rotations as a student. The attending physician expected us to know the history and details of each patient's condition and present this orally on rounds to the entire team. Missing or forgetting details was not acceptable. Our professor very clearly impressed upon the interns that, now, you are the doctor and your quality of care can potentially save the patient. These are human lives at stake, and you absolutely must know your patients inside and out. Anything less is below par.

The daily morning patient rounds were a crucible as well. By presenting to the professor in front of all of the other doctors on the ward, there was an instinctive peer pressure to demonstrate your competence. Melding the understanding of medical pathophysiology with the application to a critical patient on a mechanical ventilator is not simple, but that is part of your growth as an intern. Besides, in front of your colleagues, no one wants to embarrass themselves. Therefore, in addition to the professor's probing, insightful questions, there was also an implied standard that "average" was not good enough in medicine.

Hence, I hit the books and medical journals repeatedly. I hauled in my thick critical care book every time I was on-call, which was every fourth night. Sleep may have been at a premium between calls from nurses, but I figured that, with this book, it would either enhance my knowledge or induce a soporific effect and help me catch some sleep. I focused my studying on my patients' issues; if I did not know a certain diagnosis well, I brushed up on it. If that did not sufficiently clarify a treatment approach, I searched through the medical journals. Just like all of my fellow interns that first month of training, I strove to be as prepared as possible for morning rounds and, of course, foremost for the sake of my patients.

Part of real-world medicine, whether in the MICU or otherwise, is the possibility of death. Unfortunately, some patients will die. Every doctor will face this. And no school examination can quite prepare you for it; you need to go through the experience of your own patient dying to learn this. I vividly remember the first patient I had who passed away from his illness. He was a 70-year-old gentleman with pulmonary fibrosis, a condition from which the lungs progressively accumulate scarring, thereby compromising the ability to breathe and acquire oxygen. In the United States, approximately 16 people out of every 100,000 will develop this condition, and ultimately many will sadly die as a consequence.(67) When the fateful day came for my patient, he had several family members gathered around him in his hospital room. He knew the end was imminently near and soon was barely able to speak while on oxygen. He had previously signed a do-not-resuscitate order, indicating that he did not want any "heroic" interventions such as support from a mechanical ventilator. This was a reasonable request, as there was not any effective treatment for pulmonary fibrosis, especially for a patient already near death. Later that same day, he passed away peacefully. I recall talking with the family for close to an hour afterward, listening and attempting to console them. Even though everyone understood the prognosis, and the patient himself had elected for the do-not-resuscitate path, nothing can quite prepare you for a loved one dying.

Residency training is intentionally an arduous journey; it is meant to properly transform you from a student to a doctor so you can handle complex medical issues competently when the going gets tough. At the end of my very first day as an intern, I had wrapped up all of my tasks and given my report to the team assigned to be on-call that night about the details of my patients and what to monitor overnight. I remember feeling slightly relieved and was looking forward to getting a bite to eat at dinner. Just as I was walking to the elevator to exit the MICU, a Code Blue alarm went off, signifying that a patient's condition was acutely deteriorating and was at high risk of dying at any moment. ("Blue" refers to the blood losing oxygen, turning the skin bluish rather than the normal redness of oxygenated blood.) Nurses, doctors, and other medical personnel were rushing to one room. Technically, I was not obligated to stay and assist with the emergency, as I had already handed off my patients to my fellow intern for the night. But that is not how medicine works, and definitely not when I was in training. You don't just saunter past an emergency and ignore it. I rushed to join the resuscitation efforts, replete with chest compressions, electrical shocks to jump-start the heart, and life-saving medications—like on a television drama but without the background music. We struggled for an hour to maintain a stable heart rhythm and blood pressure, which was intermittently recovering. Thankfully, our efforts succeeded. Dinner was postponed, but who cares? The patient was still alive, and that's what matters.

Hence, the delicate processes of life and death were directly before us. We were confronting it head-on, and on a daily basis. Without a doubt, these experiences fortified that sense of great responsibility as a physician. This was as real as it gets.

Even in that first month, I felt I had learned an incredible amount as a physician. Our attending physician took us to task if we were not integrating the data cohesively enough to formulate a plan, and there was most definitely a certain amount of stress in an environment like the MICU—but through this daily exercise, we grew. We were battling to keep patients alive and comforting the families of those who sadly did not make it. The practical application of medical knowledge, the sense of responsibility instilled within me by my colleagues, and a clairvoyant conception of the standards to which doctors were held were all invaluable lessons that July of intern year.

I feel I went through medical school and the subsequent residency training at a fascinating time. It was still when patient charts were virtually always on paper, but not far before the advent of the ubiquitous electronic health record (EHR) systems of today. Doctors aligned largely with two capacious buckets: academic physicians, who worked for the university, and doctors in outpatient private practice offices. For the former, they focused on research and teaching and would partake in patient care either on assigned clinic days (often one to three days per week) or when scheduled to be the attending physicians to lead a team of residents, like my professor in the MICU.

Shortly after my training and as I started in outpatient practice, a host of changes were filtering through the healthcare sphere. We witnessed the expansion of doctors who worked in *shifts*; it was unthinkable at one time that a doctor could clock out, in contrast to when I assisted with my Code Blue on Day 1 of internship. The aphorism among physicians was "work is done when you finish your work," and therefore, there is no set time. The patient's rheumatoid arthritis is not taking the night off, is it? In addition, there was a rising tide of doctors signing up for an employed position, which also struck me as odd. As a broad characterization, doctors are opinionated and hold very clear, thought-out ideas about what constitutes optimal patient treatment. Thus, to be an employee and have someone else be a (nonphysician) boss harbors a significant risk of a conflict in viewpoints.

Another shift is the integration of computers for medical charting. As these software programs have taken over virtually every element of treating patients, from vital signs to charting to prescriptions, doctors have been increasingly inundated with time spent clicking within software programs. Nowadays I see clinicians parked in front of computers routinely, in both outpatient offices and hospital work areas. At one time, there may have been one or two computers on an entire hospital ward, and doctors would quickly write updates in a patient's chart as they saw all of their patients. Sure, we are not suddenly going to stop using computers and return to paper charts, but regardless, charting has clearly become a time sink detracting from time with patients.

From the viewpoint of many physicians, one shocker in recent years is medical residents having more and more restrictive "caps" on the number of patients they will admit while on shift. When I was in residency, we had certain rules such as 80 hours per week and the number of hours off duty after being on-call. However, while at work, there were no limitations as to how many cases you may encounter and the complexity of those patients. I recall handling multiple nights covering the emergency department, admitting patients as an internal medicine resident, when my colleagues and I were treating patients from 8:00 p.m. to 8:00 a.m. the next morning. It was merely luck of the draw; some nights were hard and others lighter. But no one can predict how many patients will seek care via the emergency room on a given night. Hence, I was incredulous when, one night a few years after training, I called the resident admitting patients to alert him about someone who required admission to the hospital. He listened to my explanation of the case and then responded calmly that he was capped for the night and could not admit any more patients on his shift. Shaking my head on my side of the phone, I requested that he clarify what he meant, and he said that after five or six admissions on a 12-hour shift, he not only was officially given a reprieve from dealing with further patients but was allowed time to nap! As a result, outpatient doctors have to potentially drive to the hospital at random times while the in-house resident is snoozing.

The concept of residency work restrictions is to lessen the chance of doctors in training becoming exhausted and, theoretically, enhancing patient safety (i.e., decreasing medical errors). These changes in recent years were devised and implemented by the Accreditation Council for Graduate Medical Education (ACGME). The intentions are reasonable, but in practice, this has not met the intended goals. In fact, a study published in 2015 investigated the impact of these residency structure changes on patient safety outcomes, residency well-being, and whether the education of trainees was being impacted. Significantly, the researchers found that there was no improvement in patient outcomes via these work restrictions. Furthermore, they found that resident education suffered (it's hard to learn when you're sleeping at work) and patient continuity of care was worse off.(129)

A number of other currents are also flowing through American healthcare. Colleagues of mine who are academic physicians are being told by departments to see more patients to increase their total insurance billings. It's becoming very commonplace that doctors throughout the country have to appeal to insurance companies to cover various procedures, studies, and treatments. The daily burden of administrative tasks is accumulating rapidly, such as a slew of forms for physical therapy, radiology scans, prescription authorizations, and the like. An astonishing thread through many of these developments is that it translates to less time with patients. (In the case of those clinicians being told to see more patients, it means less time *per patient*.)

Rather than random exceptions, these aforementioned changes reflected real trends. Furthermore, they were transforming the landscape of medical practice. However, it was not until years later into practice that I realized these alterations to medicine amounted to a fundamental clash with the cornerstones of good medicine. The heart of medical practice is the doctor caring for and endeavoring to heal the patient. But as I took a step back and contemplated these trends, I was stunned by the depth to which doctors are scrambling to adjust to these headwinds. This is what we will explore in this book, along with understanding why the existence of top-quality physicians and the sacred doctor-patient relationship itself are both under attack.

In this book, our focus is to examine the effects of the current medical system on doctors and how they practice. Crucially, I am highly concerned by how doctors *themselves* are changing. Equally alarming and directly connected to this, as we will discuss, is that the doctor-patient relationship is suffering tremendous strain. The health of this central aspect of good medicine is at risk.

As I detail the dynamics of the problematic American healthcare system as they pertain to the physician profession, we will review the pertinent systemic forces, such as how clinical practice has to adjust to health insurance companies. While I feel it is important for the public to properly understand these issues, this is not at all a judgment on health insurance companies and hospital systems as being "good" or "bad." Insurance companies, after all, have to remain profitable, as do hospitals. They are doing what they believe is needed business-wise to operate solvently within the larger system as it exists. However, I see how my physician colleagues are forced to make changes as a reaction to the system. And these changes—at least in the manner of how doctors have been forced to adjust—very often have not been positive ones and have negatively affected the doctor-patient relationship.

A recently published perspective in *The New England Journal of Medicine* commented, "A central primary care dilemma is that engaging with patients as people makes us fall behind in administrative tasks and feel more burned out, but not engaging means avoiding intimacy that would not only help the patient but keep us from feeling burned out."(128) Think about this correlation for a moment. So if we invest time with getting to know and care for our patients, we are thereby risking administrative paperwork piling up, more time later clicking within the EHR, and eventually burnout? This is not how physicians should be practicing, and it is not compatible with good medicine!

I am alarmed by how doctors themselves are changing. I have seen physician friends burning out. Nowadays, many doctors are changing jobs every few years, and consequently the patient has to start from square one with another clinician. Other older colleagues with invaluable decades of medical expertise are absolutely struggling to adapt to EHRs and how they have to treat based on what medicines the insurance company will approve. I am greatly disturbed by all of these very real trends because the future of quality medical care is at stake. The doctor-patient relationship, which is truly the heart of good medicine since time immemorial, is being fractured.

Taken together, this is a problem for all of us. Many friends of mine outside the medical field, and in my observation, vast swaths of the public, have a much rosier antiquated image of how doctors practice. Therefore, the public needs to know what is happening so we can hopefully generate creative solutions—before it is too late. I truly believe that, with the right people, right ideas, and right attitudes, we can come together as a field and both mitigate and hopefully mend these problems. The alternative—if we cannot—is frightening, for the sake of us all.

The first step in conjuring a solution is to understand the depth of the problem. Follow me, and we will take a journey to see how the stresses of the highly imperfect medical system are greatly hurting doctors, medical practice, and patients.

1

"SO, WHAT SEEMS TO BE THE PROBLEM?"

L et's face it: the proverbial system is broken. This colloquialism could apply to an inordinate number of systems-based solutions in the world today, but in this case, I am specifically referring to the American medical system. Courtesy of an expanding catalog of sources, including cost of therapies, concern for malpractice litigation and associated costs, and grossly heterogeneous medical insurance coverage, healthcare in America is very ineffectively delivered to the consumer. That is, the implementation of evidence-based medical therapeutic approaches is arduous, as patients may either not receive needed healthcare in a timely fashion or the cost of the recommended therapy is prohibitive. This is a particularly intriguing conundrum in America; after all, a highly affluent nation with a rules-based system of laws and governance should be in a prime position to deliver healthcare successfully to its citizens. And yet this does not happen.

I'm a practicing medical oncologist, and caring for patients with cancer is both complex and time-consuming but, crucially, also quite humanistically rewarding. I have loved waking up early in the morning since I was a teenager. I rationalize this on-going sacrifice of valuable sleep as the influence of my father's habit of waking early plus my intrinsic sleep cycle; I'm typically "wired" when I wake and almost literally jump out of bed. It steadies my focus and organization and allows me to keep up with work unperturbed in the predawn peace. Several months ago, I was working at my computer one morning, typing away within my electronic medical record (EMR) system, and suddenly had something of an epiphany, thinking, "This is just crazy!" Phenomena such as "click-fatigue" and aimlessly draining hours of one's time on Facebook or YouTube has been well-described as part of the modern social media dystopia. Very much akin to this, I had this visceral feeling of engaging with a similar madness as I kept clicking and clicking and clicking within the EMR on my computer. As a doctor, once you have been involved with patient care for perhaps 10 years or more, you commonly have multiple thousands of patients in your practice. Consequently, there can be seemingly no end to the number of notifications, eerily similar to those we receive day and night on our smartphones. These include lab tests, radiology reports, messages from your nurses and office staff, prescription refill requests, and communications from other consultants. You log into the EMR to check one patient's lab results, and before you know it, you click on another test result, which leads to a message you send to your nurse, and then you have to input a new order and select the covered diagnosis codes so there are no medical insurance coverage hiccups. And that's just for one patient! Hence, it truly feels like the fatigue one may experience by wandering through innumerable inconsequential posts and pointless messages in Facebook (though obviously these EMR messages are more meaningful). My children often ask me questions like "How close is the nearest black hole?" and I sometimes want to sarcastically say that the nearest one is in my office, and I routinely tiptoe near its event horizon as the extreme physics attempts to suck me in.

As I leaned back in my office chair, looking out the window, this clairvoyant realization of craziness became even more profound. I have worked at both large academic medical centers and private practice, and in large hospital systems there are often edicts that are delivered to doctors from finance departments via emails to get charts "closed" so they can submit bills to the insurance companies. Therefore, as doctors are spending hours clicking away in an EMR, sending in billing codes, and adhering to artificial timelines, no one asks about the patient! Think about it— for every minute a physician spends doing all these other activities, it aggregates into that much less time seeing patients. As I finished wading through this stream of thought, I came away with the indelible sense that this work dynamic is not sustainable ad nauseam, lest doctors truly become nauseated.

Doctors are not sufficiently politically active and not cohesive enough as a collective to successfully remedy the American healthcare system. If we were, our profession would not be saddled with the quandaries it is today. Ergo, physicians need a force greater than themselves, one that has the best interests of all patients as a guiding light. The fountain that can generate these solutions, I firmly believe, lies within the pooled wisdom and ingenuity of the American people. But a prerequisite to brilliant solutions is that the general public has to first understand the core tenets and nuances of the problem at hand.

These disturbing trends, along with a multitude of others, are negatively affecting the fundamental process of furnishing healthcare to patients. Furthermore, the sine qua non of medical care is the interaction of the doctor and the patient. Therefore, how are these stressful changes to medical practice affecting physicians? As I pondered this, several of my colleagues, all very distinct from each other, popped into my head. With the backdrop of these concerning trends, what was astonishing to me was how these discrete individuals truly crystallized how these negative forces are altering doctors and, downstream from there, the very integrity of the doctor-patient relationship!

In other words, the style of practice, cynical attitudes, stress, and job turnover that numerous colleagues who I personally know endured can be seen as the net effect of all the negative system forces at play. For example, I recall one younger family practice physician who was so concerned with rapidly declining revenues coming into the practice—and consequently he was taking a sizeable pay cut—that he left clinical medicine altogether and accepted a position at a pharmaceutical company. He shared with me that he was truly concerned he would default on his large medical school loan. Another is a good friend of mine from medical school, who I vividly recall describing his dream of being a general practitioner because he was the first doctor in his immediate family. He was smart, sociable, and thoughtful and someone who had the key qualities of an excellent primary care physician. However, as he explored his options and sought advice during med school, he switched gears to go into Emergency Medicine due to the myriad negative trends destabilizing primary care medicine. While he is an excellent ER physician, this was truly a loss for primary care medicine.

As I deliberated on these thoughts, I chatted with a few of my physician friends around the country. To my amazement, virtually all of these friends reacted by saying something along the lines of "Oh I know a guy just like that at my hospital." Thus, I quickly realized that there are numerous such individuals matching each of the various "types" of doctors I envisioned, and furthermore these trends in my research are present throughout the nation.

Therefore, from my observations and experience, I posit that doctors are changing for the worse in a number of ways, including commitment to traditional medical care, skyrocketing burnout rates, and the manner in which they practice. These doctors have transformed into flawed individuals due to the damage suffered from the veritable earthquakes (note: plural) shaking medical practice. Importantly, these physician types are drastically discordant from the caring, fatherly doctor of generations past, who has sadly gone the way of the dinosaur. How often have you gone to a doctor's appointment and felt any combination of being rushed, not having adequate time to formulate questions, all while the doctor is typing away at a computer and not looking you in the eye? I cannot say strongly enough that this is simply not an acceptable way to provide proper medical care.

These are the changes the general public needs to understand in great depth and the changes we will explore in this book. Again, without the core variables of the physician and the patient intersecting, medical care is not possible. Consequently, any solution that ultimately emerges must incorporate the calamitous problems that are directly affecting doctors. Anything less than that standard will be akin to a tapestry with loose threads, and enough tugging on these threads will make the entire fabric of American healthcare unravel. I assure you that scenario will be absolutely ruinous for us all.

To kick off, the factors that are wounding the medical system largely had their origins a few decades ago. What we will examine in this book are the consequences of this malfunctioning system for physicians, how medical practice by physicians has been adversely affected, and why this is strikingly problematic for all Americans. In other words, these harmful factors have been active in American healthcare for so long that doctors themselves are changing, and in myriad maladaptive ways.

Let's delve into cost of care first. According to the Centers for Medicare & Medicaid Services (CMS), total healthcare spending in the country has reached $3.3 trillion dollars as of 2016.(2) This therefore accounts for 17.9% of the nation's Gross Domestic Product. Drilling down further, of this staggering $3.3 trillion dollars, 75% (or about $2.5 trillion) was paid via health insurance programs, both government and private. These dollars subsequently flowed foremost to hospitals and associated services (over $1 trillion), and this category is therefore the greatest driver of healthcare expenditure in the United States. (See Figure 1.) Crucially, according to CMS, these numbers reflect a cost increase of 4.3% from 2015, or a $140 million dollar increase.

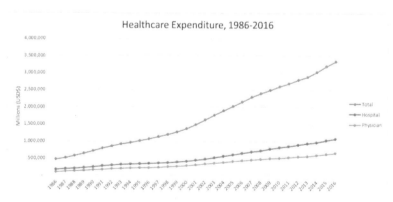

Figure 1. *Total healthcare expenditure across the United States since 1986.*
Note the widening gap between hospitals and physicians starting in 2003.

For decades, the cost of care in hospitals has been more expensive than that of physician offices in terms of dollars spent, historically due to the more medically ill hospital patient. However, there was a consistent relationship in this gap between hospital and physician costs. Then this changed around 2003, and this gap has widened substantially. (See Figure 2.)

Figure 2. *Comparison of total healthcare expenditure between hospitals and doctors. Hospital expenditures to the system are on a steeper curve since 2003.*

A third layer that is often cited is pharmaceutical, or medication, expense. With their global reach and corporate organization, pharmaceutical companies also have a generous influence in the delivery of healthcare. Prominent examples have made headlines for several years, including cancer therapies that cost more than $100,000 per year. For instance, there is a leukemia treatment, tisagenlecleucel, which according to *The American Journal of Managed Care* has a price tag (as of February 2018) in the neighborhood of $475,000 for a one-time therapy!(3) Talk about sticker shock. There have also been a number of cases of price hikes for certain drugs that also hit the patient's wallet.

These drug costs have consequences and have led to both physician and public outrage.(5) Furthermore, this has brought needed awareness to the ethical considerations and financial "toxicity" conferred upon patients. However, as can be seen by adding a third layer to the cost comparison curves over time, the total cost of pharmaceutical drug expenditures continues to be dwarfed by hospital services cost. (See Figure 3.) Of total healthcare expenditure as of 2016, medication expenses reflected 10% of the total cost. This calculates to $328 billion, which by no means is a small sum, but when examining expenditures of the entire healthcare system in America, this is an unexpectedly diminutive piece of the pie.

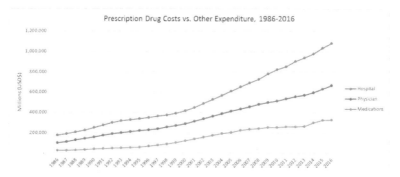

Figure 3. *Comparison of the trends of total expenditure between hospitals, physicians, and medication costs.*

Examining this national healthcare expenditure data with the relative trends among subsets is very instructive. As can be seen, 75% of the nation's dollars spent on medical services flowed from health insurance companies, with ultimately over $1 trillion to hospital systems. Therefore, the chief players in the industry have become insurance companies and hospital systems; in turn, many of the central decisions driving healthcare are being made by these two entities. It is crucial to grasp this dynamic: while medical care for an individual patient typically cannot occur in the absence of physician involvement, it is not physicians who are steering the healthcare industry. Amongst a litany of reasons, physicians simply do not possess the large-scale organization, corporate approach, or legal prowess to influence the direction of the healthcare industry on a par with these larger players. As a practicing physician, it often feels like being a Jedi Knight with a lightsaber, crusading to overthrow the Empire with their enormous resources, machinery, and firepower.

Hospital organizations and insurance companies, of course, are quite cognizant of this dynamic. In wresting power from the hands of physicians and into those of their own executives, they have escalating control of the flow of healthcare dollars. As the majority of insurance monies go to hospitals, to the tune of over $1 trillion, hospitals are also thereby incentivized to capture a larger piece of that monetary pie. For example, hospital systems can grow with more facilities and services, resulting in greater revenue. The mindset is simple: if there are $3.3 trillion healthcare dollars out there, and the troops of hospital executives are reeling in "only" $1 trillion, they are actively devising ways to increase this bottom line.

Here's the next component of the equation: as hospital systems expand their services, they gradually absorb more patients into any given system. Again, this behavior is incentivized by the tremendous sum of money flowing to hospitals. In turn, as more patients are in any given system, that system gains clout with the medical insurance companies that are covering those patients. Next, hospitals utilize this leverage, go to the negotiating table with an insurance company, and settle on a better contract. This is clearly, and not surprisingly, a very corporate style of engagement. The aftermath of this negotiation is that for the exact *same* service an independent medical practice can provide, many hospitals can both charge more fees to the patient and receive two-fold—or more—in insurance reimbursement payments!(6)

A pertinent and common example is imaging studies of the heart, such as echocardiograms (fundamentally, this is an ultrasound study). An analysis published in 2016 found that the same imaging performed in a hospital was $5,148, contrasted with only $2,862 if performed at a physician's office.(7) This $5,148 bill is footed by the combination of the patient (i.e., deductible expense and copays) plus insurance companies. The balance of this bill has been shifting toward the patient as well, as there has been a dramatic upsurge in high-deductible health insurance plans, with at least a 20% growth of such plans in 2018 compared to 2016.(8) One study found that, in 2018, the average deductible for a family is $4,331, compared to $2,198 for traditional insurance plans and, therefore, a substantial dollar figure for the average person to pay before the insurance benefit is available.(8) (Also bear in mind that most are paying a monthly insurance premium expense in addition.) Other striking investigations have seen cases of price markups for cancer chemotherapy by many multiples, simply due to the different location where the medicine was received. After all, the treatment itself is not any different. Thus, for many health insurance consumers out there, the financial pain has been accentuated in recent years.

These preceding scenarios involve the leading causes of natural death in the United States, per the Centers for Disease Control: heart disease and cancer.(9) Commenting on this trend, a physician working directly with the chief medical officer of an insurance company stated his opinion that this price uptick has occurred "without improving the quality of care."(12) Now that is both refreshingly honest and markedly alarming.

The beauty and power of language is that it can evolve to more aptly explicate a new dynamic in society. One term that has emerged to describe the consequence of this highly unfortunate relationship is "financial toxicity," which is a clever play on the medical term of "drug toxicity", when doctors analyze and discuss side effects. Thereby, this is recognition of a new socioeconomic side effect of therapy for a life-threatening illness, namely cancer. Coupled with the risk of facing one's own mortality, there is a potent psychological factor where the patient feels like they may not have a choice financially, as there is an urgency to decide upon moving forward with a recommended therapy. As a result, the opportunity to comparison shop is elusive.

The consequences of this can be severe for the patient, in terms of financial burden. In the prestigious *Journal of Clinical Oncology* in 2011, a population study compared the rate of "high health care burden"—defined as spending *more than 20%* of their income on healthcare costs plus premiums—among cancer patients. This rate was compared to two other populations: patients with other chronic illnesses and those without chronic conditions. The results are telling: 13.4% of cancer patients encountered a high healthcare burden, compared to 9.7% of those with chronic diseases and only 4.4% among those without ongoing medical conditions.(11) Data such as these have kindled increasing awareness of this issue, including the government-funded National Cancer Institute setting up a website about financial toxicity and cancer treatment.(10) However, crucially, this problem still exists.

Some readers may be logically wondering, correctly, "Wait a minute—isn't the national conversation about cutting down healthcare costs?" However, in total contrast to this lofty aim, the highly alarming trends detailed reveal the reality of what is continuing to happen in American healthcare. Pressing questions are thereby raised to the

American public: Is this the direction we want to see healthcare going? Furthermore, do we, as individual citizens, want to continue to foot this astronomical bill? In the next chapter, we will delve into how practicing physicians are attempting to answer these questions and how they are reacting to the modern dynamic of hospitals and insurance companies steering American healthcare.

2

THE DOCTOR'S AN EMPLOYEE?

At one time in the United States, the term "employed doctor" would be a laughable oxymoron to the vast majority of physicians. It is illuminating for the general public to understand why this is the case, however. Firstly, the tradition of medicine harkening back to time immemorial is that, when a person is facing a health concern, the physician uses his or her collective wisdom, knowledge, and experience to give the very best recommendation possible for that individual. In the process of offering this guidance, the doctor is not spending hours each day filling out forms, clicking literally thousands of times per day within a computer program, or obtaining an insurance company's permission on whether or not the patient can proceed with this best recommendation. Reflect for a moment on what this signifies: the doctor's mental energy and clarity is not cluttered with ancillary speed bumps, in this traditional paradigm. Therefore, by not being forced to multitask, the doctor's full attention and intellectual capabilities are able to be deployed for the patient's health. Akin to virtually any occupation requiring a high degree of technical skill and education, less distractions equates to better performance.

Furthermore, for centuries, until just the last couple decades, doctors were able to focus on patient care, charge a reasonable fee, and not succumb to distractions such as the ones mentioned. The patient's case came first and foremost. Now, some may complain about doctors' fees, just like a lawyer's rates or any other hyper-specialized professional; however, if the payment is coming straight from the wallet of the patient, market forces will lead to the rate being adjusted. For instance, as a practicing oncologist, if I set my consultation price as $2,000 per visit, I will inevitably end up having very few—if any—patients. Therefore, I will need to decrease my fee to something that is reasonable for the market.

This relationship of a doctor's professional consultation rates and patient care radically changed with the infiltration of health insurance companies. Insurance by definition is a "contract, represented by a policy, in which an individual or entity receives reimbursement against losses"; the "reimbursement" comes from the insurance company.(13) Furthermore, fundamentally, an insurance company generates profit by producing more revenue from their customers' premiums compared to the sum of the payout to customers (i.e., patients). This model is very profitable, and organizations have even reported surpluses in the billions; these were bolstered by significant rises in customers' premiums.(14)

Via effective sales of policies to patients over the past few decades, the healthcare insurance industry has grown into the trillion-dollar range.(2) This burgeoning growth is arguably even more astonishing over recent years: from 2006–2016, there has been an approximate 52% growth.(2) Have you had your health insurance premium expense go up by 15–25% in the past year, as many

Americans have faced?(15) Well, these premium rises are fueling this profit. In aggregate, per the United States Census Bureau, approximately 291 million citizens are enrolled in a health insurance plan as of 2016, with the uninsured population at 8.8%.(16)

This data is revelatory as to the current medical practice landscape. With 91.2% of Americans possessing a health insurance policy, the vast majority of doctors have no choice but to accept these insurance plans. Indeed, this has borne out in reality, with 96% of hospitals and 93% of doctors contracting with Blue Cross Blue Shield (as well as other insurance companies). It is this piece of the puzzle that truly sheds light on why medical practice has been altered so much: if 93% of doctors are accepting the payment rate from the insurance company, then the insurance company in effect is determining the income of a given doctor. This is amongst the elemental reasons many physicians see at least 20 and occasionally more than 30 patients a day. Since the doctor is no longer able to set a reasonable professional rate for services, he or she compensates by seeing more patients to account for the loss of income. Of course, there are only so many hours in a typical working day, so to increase the number of patients in a given period of time, one must therefore decrease the time with the patient! Thus, the reader can see how this equation shakes the very core of the doctor-patient relationship. The next time your physician rushes out the door in 5–10 minutes, bear this closely in mind.

So how does this herald the employed physician instead of the private practitioner? Firstly, prior to health insurance payouts driving most of a physician's income, doctors were able to utilize better professional rates (compared to insurance company reimbursement rates) to construct a working day with more time per patient. My own experience has also shown me that this is typically more satisfying for the patient and doctor. In contrast, by compressing the time with the patient and seeing more patients per day in the world of health insurance plans, a Pandora's box of negative issues has been unleashed. These include physician burnout, as we will investigate next, dealing with middlemen (for example, billing companies), and battling with insurance companies for fair reimbursement (as they are not eager to pay out monies to customers but rather want to, naturally, remain profitable).

It is not difficult to envision how less time per patient, a decrease in income, and health insurance barriers in daily practice can translate to increased risk of burnout for physicians. Consider that physicians already have long been one of the highest-risk groups for burnout, thanks to the constant burden of practicing clinicians in caring for sick and dying people; now these added stresses have exacerbated this condition.(19) Another variable that has significantly contributed to burnout is the use of electronic health record (EHR) systems. To many outside the medical profession, using a computer for medical record documentation sounds like a no-brainer, and philosophically it may very well be. However, the implementation is quite different. With many bloated and inefficient software products, often used in big hospital systems but not exclusively so, doctors spend much more time in front of computers completing patient notes and other documentation than in the past. A study published in 2017 examined over 765,000 electronic patient records and associated time stamp records over a four-year period among several hundred primary care doctors. This analysis found that approximately 50% of a physician's workday is spent in front of a computer!(20) Other research investigating the stress placed by EHRs on Emergency Medicine clinicians ("ER doctors," colloquially) found four chief factors causing frustration: remembering menu and button names and commands use, performing tasks that are not straightforward, system speed, and system reliability.(21)

These publications are but the tip of the iceberg of a burgeoning effort to understand the rising risk of burnout, and to develop strategies to mitigate it. In this undertaking, however, I caution my fellow physicians and scientists not to fall into the trap of just expecting doctors to push through the stress. This is a particularly acute point because medical training has emphasized this mentality for decades: namely, to tirelessly work, not complain, and if necessary, skip meals and sacrifice sleep. To a certain extent, these qualities are necessary to function in the job. For instance, if I receive a question from a local emergency department about my patient at 2 a.m., I need to be able to give my best answer both accurately and quickly. However, this toughness route is not the one to follow when it comes to burnout. Rather, this is an area where clinicians need education about recognizing signs and having the proper support and strategies to deal effectively with burnout. Otherwise, we would simply be accentuating the same factors that promote burnout in the first place.

Hot on the heels of rising rates of burnout and eroding job satisfaction, it is at this point in the devolution of the American healthcare system that another shift occurred. Armed with the knowledge of the frustrations of physicians, hospitals have and continue to use their pecuniary advantage garnered from superior insurance contracts to *purchase* private practices. Why? Well, fundamentally, hospitals know that most healthcare cannot be delivered without physicians. "Doctor Google" and WebMD are not effective on their own, or in another automated fashion. Philosophically, this is due to the extremely complex job requirements of a physician: the interplay of integrating the medical problems of a patient with a synthesized and thorough understanding of the medical literature, textbooks, and practice guidelines. Consequently, cases that are similar can have dramatically disparate treatment plans. Intriguingly, various attempts in the fields of artificial intelligence and deep machine learning are mining for inroads into medical treatment automation. Radiologists—doctors who give medical interpretations of imaging studies such as X-rays or CT scans—are one target; Geoffrey Hinton, a cognitive psychologist and computer scientist, professed, "It's quite obvious that we should stop training radiologists."(18) However, this has not manifested into reality, and the human physician cannot be replaced just yet.

However, if the physicians now work for them, then the hospital can bill health insurance for *all* services for a given patient! As discussed in the previous chapter, with $1 trillion of the 3.3 trillion available dollars going to hospitals, and with these institutions understandably attempting to increase their profits further, this was a clear opening to add to the "credit" side of the accounting ledger. To be clear, this approach is quite understandable from a capitalist point of view. After all, this type of strategic business thinking is why hospital corporations hire knowledgeable financial types. They are naturally tasked with developing ways to nurture the prosperity of their organization. Nevertheless, it is physicians' practice of medicine that is being directly affected. Cumulatively, these numerous stresses, such as declining income, being employed rather than one's own boss, and hours per day in front of a computer instead of patients, are affecting physicians deeply.

3

Symptoms Among Doctors

S o how are physicians coping with and reacting to these substantial changes to their daily practice? In a nutshell, not well. It is a cruel irony of the modern system that, although most medical care cannot be delivered to patients without a doctor's direct involvement, other parties are now dictating key variables of daily practice. Faced with a loss of control of their own profession, doctors are reacting in a multitude of ways. Just as the phrase "employed physician" was rarely uttered not long ago, it is just as shocking that large numbers of doctors either have left or are considering leaving traditional medicine (i.e., clinical medicine involving patient care). In fact, one survey found that up to 40% of physicians are considering exiting clinical practice within the next three years.(22)

A support structure for this has also emerged, including educational conferences helping to train doctors to successfully transition to new career paths. One such organization is SEAK, Inc, which runs numerous conferences such as the Annual Non-Clinical Careers for Physicians Conference and assorted meetings homing in on specific skill development, such as How to Excel at Your Expert Witness Deposition. According to Jackson & Coker, a physician job search and staffing firm, more than 50% of doctors change jobs in their first five years of practice. The ongoing rate is at least 9% per year—therefore, 1 in 11 doctors change jobs every year.(68)

There is also a groundswell of innumerable written articles serving as a launching pad to consider new careers while leveraging one's medical qualifications. These include the prominent American Medical Association (AMA) featuring an article entitled "The road less traveled: Nontraditional careers for physicians" in 2016 and Medscape publishing one named "'I've Had It With Medicine!' 16 Options for Second Careers." (23, 24) Among these nontraditional careers are medical device development, medical journalism (think Dr. Sanjay Gupta, a neurosurgeon who has been well-known as the chief medical correspondent on CNN), pharmaceutical industry careers, and forensic research.

These real trends serve up quite a contrast to the perception of many outside the medical field, who still imagine the doctor practicing in their local town for decades. Further, consider that doctors in the United States typically earn a lucrative income, and therefore through that lens, to risk this financial status to pursue nontraditional career paths is enormously telling. In other words, a growing proportion of doctors share a sentiment that tolerating the negative elements of clinical medicine is simply not worth the money.

One can frame this partial exodus from clinical medicine as a mature career change, a natural outcome stemming from the combination of job dissatisfaction and burnout. However, there are two remarkably germane concerns with such a professional migration. Firstly, this movement of talented and qualified physicians is still a great loss for patients. After all, we do want the best and brightest physicians treating our medical conditions, right? These are *human lives* at stake, not simply a product to sell. Secondly, the bedrock of modern medical education and training in the United States, developed on the heels of the watershed Flexner Report in 1910, is to meld analytical reasoning gleaned from the study of biomedical science with multiple years of clinical training.(27) The end result is to develop better physician clinicians and thereby promote superior patient care.

Juxtaposed with the pursuit of alternative careers is an oft-ignored dire consequence of burnout and job dissatisfaction: physician suicide. Per the American Foundation for Suicide Prevention (AFSP), male physicians commit suicide at a 70% higher rate compared with other professions, and female physicians die by their own hands at a shocking clip that is at least 250% higher than women in other lines of work!(25) The AFSP cites key drivers of physician suicide to include "workload, work inefficiency, [and] lack of autonomy." The American Medical Society reported similar data from 2015, noting the suicide rate is 40% higher for male physicians than the general population, and the female physician suicide rate is an astounding 130% higher.(26)

Thus, these trends of job turnover, declining income, and stress are not only real, but they are having a profound impact. The physician suicide rates really reverberate through my concerns about the mutated medical system and the negative impact on physicians. No, the majority of doctors are not simply living the good life on the golf course—not in the last several years. There is an excellent book written by Dr. Adam Kay, who used to be an obstetrician and gynecologist in the United Kingdom, titled *This is Going to Hurt*. He made a career change to *comedic script writing* due to the dramatically lamentable effect the medical system was having on his psyche, morale, and personal life. He touched on multiple relevant points to the current discussion, including his observation that, in the UK, "there's a mutual code of silence that keeps help from those [doctors] who need it most."(61)

While Dr. Kay was speaking about his personal experience in the UK, it is definitely applicable to the United States as well. A support system for recognizing physician stress and suicide risk is direly needed in the US for physicians. Whatever laughably loose shards are available currently are woefully inadequate. In my experience, I have not heard one person, hospital, or university *ever* ask me about how I was handling job stress. And bear in mind, I am an oncologist and deal with patients dying, sadly too often.

In addition to physician job stress, another key trend is declining income. The decision to become a doctor remains a "calling," I would argue. Dr. Adam Kay revealed this beautifully in his book, with the point that no one would put up with the rigors of medical training, juggling life-and-death decisions, and personal sacrifice (including affecting one's relationships and work-life balance) if one did not intrinsically enjoy helping patients on some level. However, money is inextricably linked to real-life concerns, regardless of your metaphysical calling.

In the parlance of economics, job "churn" or turnover is one of the most effective ways to increase one's income and other monetary benefits. Now, the American job market on the whole recovered well from the recessionary effects of the turbulence of 2008, and the unemployment rate has reached very low levels. In September of 2018, the jobless rate in the US was 3.7%, which was the lowest since

1969.(56) Furthermore, for physicians, the job market remains quite robust, such that, particularly if one is willing to relocate, there are no shortages of positions with very high compensation packages. The numbers are impressive: in 2018, five metropolitan areas had physician job growth of 17% or more. Perhaps more astonishing is that six metropolitan areas had average pay increase 12% or more compared to just the prior year in 2017.(57) The United States Department of Labor forecasts an overall growth for the physician market to rise a further 13% by 2026.(58)

With this landscape of job opportunities, and with the substantial negative forces in healthcare affecting how doctors practice traditional medicine, it is quite natural that doctors will therefore gravitate toward accepting a new job elsewhere. As some career advisors have proclaimed, "Any job can impel a worker to look for greener pastures if the boss is a brute, compensation is meager or recognition is infrequent."(59) All of these cited factors affect clinical medicine, with the clarification that physician compensation may not be meager, but declining incomes (or "undercompensation" relative to the burden of work) are a significant driver of job turnover.

Doctors have another considerable ongoing financial concern: repayment of medical school loans. Bear in mind that school loans in the United States constitute unforgiveable debt. So if one is burned out or unsatisfied in a given job, the doctor has to find other employment fairly quickly, lest they fall behind on loan payments. Furthermore, the total amount of the med school loan is truly like a second mortgage. Per the Association of American Medical Colleges (AAMC), "the median debt was $200,000 in 2018," and among students who attended a private medical college, "21% of students have debt of $300,000 or more."(102)

Therefore, if physicians have plentiful options for jobs in the market, why should they stick around somewhere, mired in tangible stress and ungrateful administrators? And as mentioned earlier, greener pastures do not necessarily imply chasing the greenback; the large number of doctors leaping into nonclinical careers is evidence of this. Dr. Kay phrased it well in his book, stating that "once upon a time, these people [doctors] were rescheduling their own weddings for this job."(61) In stark contrast, we have dramatically high turnover as well as physicians leaving traditional medicine altogether.

Human resource surveys have revealed another variable that helps inform us as to why doctors make such choices: a "stronger mission."(60) Recall that most tragic of consequences of job dissatisfaction and burnout: physician suicide. Therefore, finding more meaning in one's work can go a long way into assuaging these factors.

What about those individuals who remain within clinical medicine, in spite of the current healthcare system? Well, a first principle is that the days of the caring, dedicated family doctor are virtually obsolete. If you find one, you are lucky, and she is a relic from a different era. More specifically, these are the doctors who really take the time to know you, where you work, and your family. They place tremendous value on not making the patient feel rushed and allow you to feel comfortable enough to openly have a dialogue about your concerns. Sure, they have their personal lives too, but they're happy to discuss a symptom by phone if needed. I know a few fabulous colleagues who are still like this; they are truly fighting the good fight.

However, from my personal experience, discussions with multiple colleagues, and research, countless doctors have been compelled to make striking changes as a reaction to today's medical system and its litany of problems. Broadly, they fall into seven major types of doctors that I have observed. We are going to explore each of these individuals and why their practice and professional work has transformed. We will also see why some have exited clinical medicine, others burn out trying to futilely fight the system, and the remainder suffer frustration and professional disillusionment. Through this journey, we will shed a bright light on why the changes these doctors have been forced to make are harmful to good medical practice and, consequently, deeply unhealthy for the very heart of medicine: the doctor-patient relationship.

4

METAMORPHOSIS

D id you ever dream of going to medical school? Well, here's your chance. In the preceding chapters, we have scrutinized the current state of the problem and examined its effects. We've seen the astonishing rise of the business of medicine into a trillion-dollar industry and how insurance companies and hospital systems have become the key players driving healthcare. Consequently, the daily practice of medicine has been profoundly reorganized into five-minute visits, to the detriment of both patients and doctors. Coupled with declining insurance payments for the doctor's professional expertise and deteriorating professional satisfaction, rates of burnout have significantly risen. Many doctors are actively leaving clinical medicine. The confluence of these factors has spiraled into creating multiple types of doctors—with differential and often problematic effects on your health and healthcare.

So put on your white coats and grab your stethoscopes. We're going to take a walk through the hospital ward of the American medical system and present each case so we can clearly define the problems inherent to these various types of doctors. The doctors are now the patients.

5

THE IDEALISTIC DOCTOR

Dr. Bill Osler is a 32-year-old gentleman originally hailing from a Maryland suburb, who was previously in good health until about two years ago. He attended Johns Hopkins for medical school, which has long been considered one of the best schools in the country. He truly felt like the proverbial local boy who "did good" and, after he completed his training, was excited to enter primary care practice not far from where he grew up. He often heard his own parents complain about their difficulties with issues like cost of care, but Dr. Osler swore to himself that there was no way he could be like that. The patient was going to come first, and he was going to practice to the best of his ability every day.

Over the past two years in practice, however, Dr. Osler has felt increasingly stressed and frustrated. Let's go through a day in his life—umm, practice. Is there a difference? It appears not, for our gentleman here, seeing that he is frequently completing patient charts until 9:00 p.m. The staggering number of times he is clicking boxes in the EHR seems unexpectedly different from his residency training. He used to love playing volleyball; now, there's simply not time. Not surprisingly, as a consequence, Dr. Osler notes that he is often tired walking into the office in the morning. When he first started practicing, he relished thinking of each patient's medical conundrums and scouring the literature as needed to answer questions. In contrast, he nowadays has been almost dreading looking at the patient schedule. His enjoyment in conversing with his patients remains intact. But what scares him is that when he reads the names, what flashes before his eyes is first the "obstacles" in their cases—such as insurance denials—rather than the salient medical problems.

One recent disturbing episode that precipitated his admission to our ward was the insurance denial of a recommended antihypertensive medication. Dr. Osler was proud of how he was able to diagnose his patient's subtle symptoms of premature heart disease, and the local cardiologist fortunately was able to successfully stabilize the patient's coronary arteries with three stents. Upon the patient returning to see Dr. Osler, he recommended an antihypertensive medication based on impressive data published in the New England Journal of Medicine last year. To his surprise, however, the patient called the following day that the medication needed a prior authorization, and without this, it would cost about $285 per month, which the patient flatly stated he could not afford. Our good physician bulled forward, filling out the prior authorization form, and two weeks later, a letter from the insurance company said the request was denied, stating the medicine "does not meet medical necessity." Alternative older blood pressure medications were listed that were on the patient's insurance formulary. Dr. Osler became irritated at the thought of prescribing what he felt was an inferior treatment in spite of the best evidence-based medicine. Even worse, his patient also received a copy of the denial letter, and he then missed his next two appointments. Dr. Osler called multiple times—personally—with no call back. He recalls slamming his desk with his hand in frustration, blankly staring at the wall. A smiling picture posted on Facebook of one of his old medical school friends working on a cruise ship as an infectious disease physician came to mind suddenly. It hit him then that something had to change.

***

D r. Osler's predicament exemplifies common tribula- tions of the "idealistic doctor." While often younger in age, this is not necessarily so. I was speaking with a fellow oncologist in North Carolina who had been in practice over 25 years. We were commenting on some of the absurdities we had encountered with insurance denials on a recently approved chemotherapy medication when he paused and said, exasperated, "Why can't we just see patients? I just want to see patients." He was alluding to the dream of be- ing magically able to select the best drug for an individual patient, irrespective of the cost. I recall nodding silently, thinking how nice but unrealistic it would be to simply ig- nore insurance boundaries and cost of therapies. It's like a medical board certification exam. I have never seen any question on cost or insurance. The queries purely focus on the medicine and science. Knowledge of the medical sci- ence constitutes one of the pillars of treating patients, along with attributes such as ethics, but accomplishes vir- tually nothing when dealing with real-world obstacles.

This dovetails into another feature of medical training. In residency programs, curricula focus on areas such as tri- aging patients, mechanical ventilator settings, board exam preparation, and research.(62) Clearly all of these are core skills for becoming a practicing physician, but almost no attention is given to developing vital real-world skills to tackle insurance denials, high patient copays, and navi- gating "the system" in general. In reference to these latter skills, doctors are expected to sink or swim after complet- ing their training. Accordingly, when one is not educated on the inimical nuances of the system, expectations are formed that are both unrealistic and rather nebulous. Therefore, this leads to the first of the maladaptations by doctors. The discordant emphasis of training coupled with the obstacles faced in clinical practice leads certain doctors to retreat to the very idealism they were taught in medical school and training. Just like Dr. Bill Osler in the case above, the cumulative frustrations of daily practice inspire certain physicians to focus on what they can control: the pure medical science. This tact revolves around considering the possible diagnoses and logically examining and testing the patient to arrive at the correct treatment.

While superficially this idealism may not seem unreasonable, my surmise is that this tact is maladaptive, for a slew of reasons. For starters, the world of residency training is that of an isolated silo. When an internal medicine resident requires a surgical evaluation of their patient, they page the surgical resident in the hospital. Minimal thought is given to whether or not the patient will be satisfied with the particular surgical resident who will assess the patient's case, or the skill of the attending surgeon. This ill preparation translates to many young physicians committing mistakes in this arena. Succinctly, the idealistic physician struggles to get patients from point A to point B in the medical system, due to the lack of a cohesive and effective network.

The power of your professional network, as a physician, has at least three central positive features. Firstly, the network is efficient. If one's patient has suffered a serious ankle injury, it is highly beneficial and optimal to have the patient rapidly referred to an orthopedic surgeon specializing in ankle injuries. Particularly with the nature of the medical issue in this example, this path is clearly best for the patient. There are a few ways this handoff can occur. Most efficient is directly calling a specific orthopedist whom you work with and know well; typically, after a few minutes of discussing the salient issues, the surgeon will personally expedite the appointment for your patient. This often will result in the patient being seen by the specialist within one to three days. Alternatively, the orthopedic clinic has an excellent staff that is consistently capable of quickly booking the patient with the appropriate doctor, without a personal phone call. The least desirable permutation of a referral is that, upon making the request, the orthopedic clinic's staff is notoriously slow in scheduling the patient, leading to a delay in your patient seeing the requested specialist for at least a few weeks or even more than a month.

The second key characteristic of an effective network is the patient being satisfied. This involves the consulting physician having good bedside manner and instilling enough confidence in the patient that she feels she has been sent to the best doctor for her specific problem, and therefore, there is a sound reason to believe she is on the path to being healed. Anyone who has dealt with an urgent medical issue will appreciate the intangible value of the doctor projecting confidence and reassurance.

The third, and arguably most important, feature is that after the patient is scheduled and subsequently happy with the consulting doctor, the medical course of action decided upon is consistent with your (the referring physician's) treatment philosophy. In other words, the consulting doctor did not completely contradict your recommendation or even inadvertently disparage your care for the patient. This is a subtle but vital distinction from a minor difference of opinion; the latter can happen all the time, such as a cardiologist recommending a different antihypertensive medication than the internist. The patient-doctor relationship is based on trust and confidence. Therefore, if a radically dissimilar treatment path is chosen or, worse, if the consulting doctor speaks in a manner that denigrates the prior care of the patient, that confidence and trust is at least partially eroded. That is not promoting a particularly salubrious relationship with one's patient.

Young physicians simply do not have a robust network possessing such attributes. They may consciously or subconsciously realize this but, in their idealism, feel that they will have the patient successfully get better via a brute force mentality. This physician is thinking, "My patient needs an orthopedic surgeon. I've ordered the referral in the computer, and I'm sure someone—I have absolutely no idea who or when—will schedule the patient with the right doctor. My patient will get better and then come back to me happily and continue her normal care."

This is akin to believing a great quarterback can win the Super Bowl without a strong offensive line, without sure-handed receivers, and with a subpar running back. It's a fantasy. Sure, you may throw a touchdown occasionally but not consistently—and you're definitely not winning the Super Bowl. By analogy, you are trying to win in spite of the system; that is a core problem with the idealistic physician. No matter how hard you may try to fight the system, once you get sacked enough and lose enough games, you eventually start dreaming of playing for a better team—ergo, job turnover.

I am no exception with respect to this paucity of a network as a young doctor. Less than six months into practice, I had a patient who had a tumor that needed surgical removal, and I referred the patient to one of the local surgeons who had a prominent "name" in the field. It seemed like a reasonable course of action, at the time. To my great surprise, the patient called me after the surgical consultation and told me how "the guy was a complete jerk" and that he refused to follow up with that surgeon. I called the surgeon to find out what happened, and he was not only unfriendly, but he spent half the conversation on the phone arguing with me that I called my male patient "she" instead of "he," when I assuredly did not. A surgeon fixated on arguing about pronouns is a highly unusual event, I can state with confidence. After this incident, I have not sent a single other patient to that surgeon in over a decade. The real error, however, is a consequence of not having strong professional relationships in place to effectively get the patient from point A to point B. I had no idea about the surgeon's personality, nor his treatment philosophy—just that he had name recognition. I still remember feeling bad when I heard from my patient.

Thus, the idealistic physician is ultimately at the mercy of the dysfunctional medical system. Moreover, even after getting through seeing all the patients, writing prescriptions, and ordering lab tests, you finally have to park yourself in front of your computer and complete your patient charts for the day. As mentioned earlier, a 2017 study reviewing time-stamped records of 765,000 patient charts found that doctors spend around 50% of their day charting. So it's quite normal that, in aggregate, our idealistic Dr. Osler spends three to five hours with patient documentation—with the bulk of this occurring *after* he sees his patients! No wonder he's up until 9 p.m. finalizing charts and then feeling tired the next day. Consequently, time for leisure pursuits is sharply limited. Our Dr. Osler used to play volleyball avidly; this is but a daydream now.

The idealistic physician is thus often resigned to the maladaptation of a brute-force attack from within the medical system. He'll continue to push harder, see patients day after day, drown in patient documentation, and sacrifice personal pleasures. Sure, Dr. Osler can continue seeing patients this way, perhaps even for a few years. In the vein of the quarterback who keeps getting sacked due to subpar teammates, the candle of enthusiasm eventually whittles out. This situation will decay into frustration and burnout, which is but a short slippery slope away from seeking other and hopefully better job opportunities.

Another wrinkle that can stress this dynamic even further are the priorities of the hospital management with respect to the physician's specialty. For example, a colleague of mine was working for a hospital-owned endocrinology practice. She had two other partners, and the group had no shortage of patients, caring for approximately 20 patients each per day. However, the hospital management was in the midst of a fight with the cardiologists at the institution. As many people may be aware, cardiology is a generally much higher revenue-generating specialty than caring for diabetes. Therefore, not shockingly, the cardiology conundrum took overwhelming precedence over any problems faced by other hospital-employed physicians. In the process of this dispute, the cardiologists revolted en masse and took their patients and business to a competing hospital. This set off a financial shock to the hospital, virtually overnight. Consequently, when my colleague's endocrinology group lost their nutritionist due to a job change, and then logically asked to initiate a search for a new nutritionist, the hospital administration's response was, paraphrased, "We'll get to you when we get to you. There are bigger fish to fry right now!"

As a brief aside, the aforementioned revenue difference applies to both physicians and hospitals—in contrast, it is a tremendous market for pharmaceutical companies, with 2 of the 10 top-selling medications worldwide being diabetes products. These two prescriptions grossed over $5 billion each! (54, 55)

So for these endocrinologists, their support system sucked. And who winds up doing the nutritional counseling in the midst of a 20-patient day? This task gets dumped on the doctor, of course! There's no extra compensation—just more work, more stress, and more charting to complete every day. Moreover, ponder how realistic is it for a physician to deal with all these facets of her job, and also dedicate enough time to each patient? With the insurance pressures and declining reimbursements as detailed previously, in a nutshell, the answer is that it is simply not possible. Ultimately, my endocrinology colleague sought and accepted a new job in a different state.

In my view, a job change, whether to another practice or to a nontraditional career path, is one of the few realistic options to salvage the idealistic physician's plight. This is one major route by how patients lose their doctor. As with most occupations, to choose an option where one breaks the proverbial mold is psychologically a more daunting opportunity to tackle. Increasing numbers of physicians are venturing into nontraditional medical careers, but the majority continue to try their hand at clinical medicine. Therefore, he or she will accept a position at another practice, not uncommonly completely out of the local vicinity where one was practicing.

The latter point—a substantial location change—occurs for two key reasons. Firstly, most practices have a noncompete clause in contracts, so for a specified period of time (often one to two years) the physician cannot open up shop across the street and have all his patients follow him. He could theoretically wait out this one- to two-year time period, but most will understandably want to move to another position as soon as possible for income reasons. The second reason for moving to a new geography is the allure of starting fresh, and the often unrealistic thinking that the grass is greener elsewhere. The system problems we have discussed thus far do have local variances, but many key similarities remain regardless of being in a different state.

The net result of the idealistic physician's maladapted approach to medicine is that he becomes increasingly disillusioned and incurs a considerable risk of burnout. This starts him on a slippery slope to a job change. A new position, particularly in a sufficiently distant geography, also compounds the problem of not having a robust professional network. The doctor's fresh start at a new practice may be invigorating in the short term, but now you have to break into the local medical community and develop these vital contacts from scratch. In other words, the professional network is back to square one, and therefore, the benefit of prompt care with satisfied patients remains elusive. Lastly, and crucially, think of the loss of continuity of care for patients with a physician move. Sure, other physicians can assume a patient's medical care, but I can tell you strongly from personal experience that it is never the same as a deep holistic understanding of a person's health, like when you have been with the patient from the start.

The other viable option is joining the exodus to a nontraditional medical position. In the case of my experienced local oncologist colleague in North Carolina, he left active practice and went to a clinical research organization. These are firms that contract with pharmaceutical corporations to administer the logistics and oversight of clinical trials in patients. Such roles often afford doctors a much more favorable work-life balance, not being on call, and none of the headache of battling insurance companies. However, from the perspective of a fellow clinician, I believe this is an example of a good, intelligent doctor lost to a role outside of patient care. In effect, this is America's "doctor capital" being eroded.

Thus, for the idealistic doctor, he faces potent headwinds in his quest to treat the patient in the best tradition of his medical training. This clash of medical training preparedness against the realities of practice obstacles crests with the physician being forced to adjust. With the resultant maladaptive dogged focus on striving to swim through these currents, the idealistic physician unfortunately takes his first steps on the slippery slope to burnout and job change.

Case Progress Update:
Dr. Osler was admitted to the physician rehabilitation unit now 43 days ago. He was last observed this morning combing through physician job opening websites. His condition remains guarded.

6

THE INTERNATIONAL MEDICAL GRADUATE

Our next patient is Dr. Madhava, a 49-year-old lady who joined a busy five-physician internal medicine practice in Alabama about three years ago. She emigrated from India relatively recently and completed residency training in Iowa prior to her move to Alabama. In speaking with her, she admits that her current practice locale is strikingly not what her relatives in India envision; they are picturing her working on Fifth Avenue in Manhattan across from Central Park. She has adapted to her new environs fairly well, however, and works hard in the practice, seeing about 22 patients per day. Her partners admire her diligence but are quietly surprised about how several local doctors are loyally referring patients to her, in spite of being relatively new—and lacking local roots.

When her patients first come to her exam room, they don't see glitzy residency graduation certificates from Baylor or Cleveland Clinic like a few of the other physicians have. Rather, a lone frame from a city hospital in Iowa adorns the wall. There are a few who switched their care to another doctor in the group due to her accent and relatively rapid speech tempo being difficult to understand, a more common occurrence with some of the older patients. Nevertheless, her patients on the whole seem to be satisfied after discussion with her and impressed by her confidence and attention to detail.

Between patients, she diligently plugs away at her patient charting. Others in the practice notice she doesn't typically congregate at the nursing area, laughing like two of her partners tend to do. She often is reticent to attend parties after work hours but has been opening up in this regard over the past several months.

Her physician partners shared with us that, though they are appreciative of Dr. Madhava's hard work and her not complaining about being on-call when requested, they do worry if she is "overdoing it" and risking burning out. They are sincerely hoping she does not burn out, as it has been historically quite difficult recruiting physicians to their part of the state. It took nearly a year to fill the position that Dr. Madhava did. Privately, she too has been more aware of feeling the grind of daily busy practice and has been wondering to her family if any greater fulfillment from a medical career is possible or not.

***

S tories like these play out in cities and towns of all sizes and in all states across America. Here's the secret that most Americans do not know: international doctors hoping to practice in the US have to *repeat* residency training in the US. Furthermore, to get admitted to a residency, they have to have substantially higher test scores than US medical school graduates. Ergo, only the crème de la crème have even a chance of scoring an interview at a residency program. Conversely, if an international graduate applied while possessing the average score of US graduates, he or she would truly have no chance at getting the position.

This high bar for admittance has a few natural consequences. Firstly, it is clear that, on the whole, only the best foreign graduates—based on test scores—can bag a residency training spot. Secondly, because it is ultracompetitive to enter a training program after graduating from abroad, the international physician is happy to get a position, wherever in the country that may be. Among medical specialties, there is a hierarchy of selectiveness for training spots, and specialties such as dermatology, radiology, orthopedic surgery, and neurosurgery require a resume replete with higher scores, research experience, and strong letters of recommendation (highly preferably from prominent physicians in the field). It is arduous for the physician emigrating from India, for instance, to tick these requisite boxes. This is due both to having a disparate educational system (where test scores are disproportionately prioritized over components like research work) and not having the connections to obtain the thrust of a glowing letter of recommendation from an academic professor. As a result, it is very unrealistic for the typical international graduate to go into dermatology. Therefore, they will gravitate toward fields where there is both a better chance of acceptance, and those that have a track record of having residents from international medical schools. These fields commonly include primary care specialties, with Internal Medicine being the most common, followed by Family Practice.(43) Over time, this dynamic has resulted in a multitude of hospitals that not only are willing to accept foreign medical graduates (i.e., those who have the best test scores) but are often filled almost exclusively with graduates from abroad.

This helps ameliorate at least three large-scale issues in American healthcare. For one, there has been a physician shortage building for decades due partly to the rising population in the nation, as well as the increasing older set.

Studies have forecast that this shortage will total an estimated 125,000 physicians by the year 2025.(44) Hence, turning to international graduates to fill this need is beneficial. Additionally, the luxury of having applicants with top scores helps ensure the doctors entering the American workforce are those of high quality. As most often these graduates are going into primary care specialties, this also bridges a gap, as many US medical graduates lean to subspecialization (such as cardiology, for example), which is a more lucrative career path. Thirdly, there is an uneven geographic distribution of physicians in the United States, such that certain states and rural communities typically have fewer physicians (and even lower numbers of subspecialists). As international medical graduates, at least initially, are working while on an H1 work visa, they often find employment in these areas that both have greater need and are willing to sponsor doctors on a visa.

English proficiency is clearly a salient issue for medical practitioners. A cornerstone of being an effective physician is strong communication skills. For this reason, the United States Medical Licensing Examination (USMLE) taken in medical school includes a practicum where you are graded on your interviewing and counseling skills with patients. Therefore, beyond excellent exam results, the prospective residency applicant must have a certain command of English language. Not surprisingly, the most prevalent countries where the foreign graduates hold citizenship are ones that have a strong English language component in their schooling. Four of the top five nations of origin are India, Canada, Pakistan, and Nigeria—interestingly all former British colonies at one point in history.(45)

Further eye-opening is the experience the international graduate has to endure to reach the point of a US residency training program. Due to the de facto prerequisite to obtain the highest possible score on the USMLE, dedicated study for 6–12 months, if not longer, is needed to ensure they are fully prepared. Everything is riding on the USMLE result. One must bear in mind a few critical variables: For one, studying for months on end for a chance to become a licensed doctor in America places significant stress on these graduates. Most people cannot conceptualize the mental focus needed to prepare for a year just for an examination, especially with the outcome being so life-altering. Relevant context, from my personal experience, is that I studied for three *weeks* for the USMLE test, as did virtually all of my classmates having graduated from a US medical school. In fact, I can honestly say I have difficulty grasping this prolonged combination of focus and great tension. Moreover, during these months of stress, a practical issue is that these foreign graduates have to generate income. Often, these physicians will work in a variety of nonmedical professions to pay their living expenses. I have known friends and colleagues who have been employed as car mechanics, limousine drivers, and grocery store clerks. Most will be in their mid- to late-twenties, and in stark contrast to the millennial stereotype, they generally will not have the luxury of having their parents support them financially while they come to America to study for a year for a decisive examination.

The final math is striking. After enduring the psychological stress of months of studying, shouldering the burden of the make-or-break nature of the USMLE, and potentially being employed in an unrelated and random field in a new country, the question is, what is the success rate of this path? According to data from the National Residency Matching Program (NRMP), which is the primary mechanism through which residency applicants get matched to training hospitals, only 49.5% of international medical graduates get accepted into a residency. Dramatically, the success rate of US medical graduates is a sparkling 94.4%.(46)

Astounding, isn't it? More than 50% of foreign graduates will not successfully garner a residency spot. For those who make it, it radically alters their career horizon. These individuals will be doctors in America, which essentially guarantees a certain income threshold and standard of living. Buoyed by their success at gaining admittance to a training program, these individuals can carry this modus operandi of hard work into daily practice. Philosophically, they are realists, not idealists, and the experiences one must endure to get accepted to a residency program reinforce this realism. In a general sense, many immigrants have to be realists if they aspire to be successful in a new country.

But what about those who don't make it? Some will make another attempt at the USMLE examination, if not multiple attempts. Again, be mindful of the time commitment, psychological pressure, and often financial stress of tackling this mountain once more. Others will return to their native countries and resume work there. And another segment will pursue other medical career options, such as radiology technicians, laboratory scientists, and nurses.

When I was in residency, there was one exceptionally outstanding nurse in the intensive care unit of the hospital. He was in his late forties, born in China, and extremely competent. As a physician, even when one is still in residency training, you can quickly notice those nurses who have a very clear grasp of clinical issues. Particularly in the intensive care unit, where patients are the most critical, such superb individuals rise to the fore. My friends and I would joke that we sometimes would fight to be assigned to the patients to whom this nurse was tending, because the nurse was so good we would barely got bothered with any pages. Then one time on a night shift, a couple of us were talking with this nurse, teasing him good-naturedly, "Are you sure you aren't secretly a pulmonologist?" (In the ICU, pulmonary & critical care physicians are the attending doctors for patients.) In response, he deadpanned quite seriously, "I actually am a doctor—or rather was, in China!" Then he expounded on his educational background and how, due primarily to language difficulties, he was not able to achieve a sufficient score on the USMLE test. This prompted his decision to go into nursing, as he was motivated to be a clinician. At some time around 1 a.m. on a night shift, we could viscerally feel the epiphany as the pieces now fit together.

It is crucial to understand these nuances of the backgrounds and path of international medical graduates— particularly as these doctors are comprising a rising tide among the ranks of the workforce. Akin to the Idealistic Physician in the previous chapter, this powerful trend of foreign graduates reshaping the landscape of physicians is in effect a maladaptation due to system forces. Sufficient numbers of US graduates, while educated at world-renowned institutions, are on the whole simply not selecting primary care as their specialty. This is due to the loss of income relative to subspecialists (who, by the way, have also suffered a loss of income but still earn more), along with the slew of the negative variables experienced in clinical practice by the Idealistic Physicians. Ergo, it is no wonder that Dr. Madhava's Iowa hospital certificate was not recognized by her patients. In fact, the residency training location is not a reliable marker of quality at all in these individuals.

There are a number of other challenges faced by foreign medical graduates, also, stemming from the dual potent forces of being an immigrant and a resident physician. A study conducted by Yale University in 2011 is particularly fascinating, as the authors interviewed 25 foreign graduates about the unique demands encountered.(37) The specific stories and quotes from the interviewees are quite edifying. One doctor crystallized the impediments to integration well, stating, "The new terminology, the language, the technology... The basic foundation of knowledge was there, but catching up with all these things at once was overwhelming." One can readily sympathize with the stress of such circumstances.

Another doctor in this study lamented the conflation of stylistic differences and ability. "We were perceived to be different and... it was a very turbulent year. They related it all to incompetence... Some of us were even called antisocial."(37) This physician went on to hypothesize that most of these "differences" were cultural variances. The directness of speaking, facial expressions, and humor is often drastically distinct in other nations.

Enduring subtle derision was a common theme as well. "Foreign medical graduate" is abbreviated colloquially as FMG; some of those interviewed would overhear American-trained doctors commenting, "Oh, he's an FMG," with the connotation of being substandard in some respect. One individual had an American colleague state, "You are not like them... you're better," which still carries the undertone of being insulted.(37) It is akin to someone saying, "You're not like the other Indian doctors, you're better." Phrased in that context, it is plain how an offhand remark like that can be offensive.

Others were particularly cognizant of the contrasts of living in America compared to their native country. While doctors, as healers of the sick, are typically afforded ample respect in most cultures, the degree of financial affluence can vary quite a bit. As one foreign graduate observed, "Me being here doesn't do anything for my people... Even after acquiring this knowledge, I can't help my people. I'm frustrated."(37) This is also related to the issue of a "brain drain," where the top doctors from a given nation leave for the United States, and therefore this is a loss for the doctor's native land. In a sense, it also negates the efforts of a local school university to educate the populace to productively contribute to their immediate society.

Is there another channel to this brain drain, where the United States can gain ideas at a more system level, beyond the individual clinician? Might that illuminate possible solutions for at least some issues? Let's break out the microscope and delve into healthcare delivery of a few other nations, namely the United Kingdom and Canada (countries from where many foreign graduates emigrate).

Let's take Canada first. As a practicing physician in this age of highly polarized politics, I hear enormous numbers of myths from both a positive and negative perspective about the Canadian healthcare system. Among the founding goals of our northern neighbor's approach is to control costs. One of the most crucial facts when considering the applicability of another country's approach is the total population. An estimated 37 million people reside in Canada currently, in contrast to about 328 million in America. That's a staggering discrepancy: thus, the US has over 12 times the population and 300 million more people. (38, 39) Fewer citizens also translates to much less total cost of medical care, and this population difference is an enormous barrier in translating our neighbor's approach to the United States.

A second key myth is that Canadians have a single-payer scheme, such that a Medicare-like system foots the bill for everyone's medical needs. This is not accurate. While the Canadian government does provide state-run health insurance, many citizens have to additionally possess private health insurance to pay for many costs, such as prescription medications. It is estimated that the government insurance pays for 70% of the costs overall.(40) While Canada has performed admirably in controlling cost of medical care, it is not a system where costs are somehow fully covered without any personal money or private insurance supplementation.

The double-edged sword of controlling costs is that certain services may have to be delayed, including doctor visits and surgical operations. This is an inevitable issue that the Canadian government has to contend with, as the overall healthcare expenditure in Canada is about 10% of the gross domestic product, or about $165 billion. (40, 41) Ergo, this is not a cheap venture their government has assumed. Furthermore, if costs are to be controlled within the sphere of increasingly expensive medical technologies and pharmaceutical drugs, patient evaluations and treatments must inevitably be rationed and, hence, span longer periods of time. Everyone simply cannot get every treatment right away, lest expenses swiftly skyrocket. A number of studies have examined wait times for Canadians, including the Frasier Institute, a think tank based in Vancouver that examines government actions that impact Canadians' quality of life.(47) In their report published in December 2017, their survey found that the median wait time from a referral by a general practitioner to receipt of treatment by a specialist was 21.2 weeks, which is slightly longer than the 2016 metric of 20.0 weeks. That's at least five months of waiting for a treatment. Quite remarkably, the same measurement was 9.3 weeks in 1993.

The wait times and, hence, access-to-care barrier is a valid and true concern in the Canadian health system. This does not mean the quality of treatment or physicians is at all substandard, but clearly *time* is a vital variable in ameliorating medical illness. Conversely, a delay in diagnosis or treatment can have profound consequences. Now, to what extent patients need to be patient is rather heterogeneous depending on medical specialty and province of residence. The Frasier Institute found that the longest wait was with orthopedic surgery, at 41.7 weeks—ergo over 10 months—whereas the shortest was for cancer treatment, which was 3.2 weeks.(47) From a geographical viewpoint, citizens in Ontario had the shortest wait for both a specialist consultation and receipt of therapy. The longest delay in obtaining a specialist opinion on a case was in New Brunswick, at 26.6 weeks, which therefore is more than six months. Further underscoring that this is a real and concerning matter is that, in 2004, Canada's first ministers (analogous to governors of states in the US) pinpointed five priority areas to reduce wait times, including cancer treatment, heart disease, and joint replacements.(48)

Part and parcel with wait times is the added layer of not being able to readily "shop" for doctors. In America, if you are willing to hop in the car and drive, one can call up virtually any clinic, including that of a specialist, and schedule an appointment. This ability is taken for granted in the United States, as almost everyone is aware that, as long as they can pay the doctor's fees, they can obtain an appointment. In Canada, people have the freedom to choose any primary physician, but specialist appointments are relatively restricted due to both lack of specialists and because "gatekeepers" must authorize a referral to see a specialist. Cue the wait time clock.

There is also the additional nuance that patients are covered by the provincial health insurance for their fees, but higher specialist expenses may induce out-of-pocket bills, which are not reimbursed by the government plans. While this is not an absolute barrier, in a nation that has primary doctor visits covered fully, it can be a mild shock to the mindset.

Next, let's sail across the Atlantic to examine the United Kingdom's National Health Service (NHS). From a population perspective, the UK is between Canada and the United States, with an estimated 66 million residents as of 2017, per Great Britain's Office of National Statistics.(49) As the name suggests, the English system confers automatic coverage for its legal residents. For necessary medical care (as opposed to elective), such as primary care visits and emergency department treatment, patients are fully covered for costs via NHS. We discussed the prickly landscape of cost control and wait times that Canada has to navigate, and propelled by a number of reforms to privatize portions of the national health insurance, the United Kingdom has been able to make significant headway in counteracting some of these pitfalls. As of 2015, an "estimated 10.5 percent of the U.K. population had private voluntary health insurance," facilitating more rapid acquisition of elective treatments and procedures. (50, 51) This has had the desired effect of enhanced access to care over the past several years, particularly for elective procedures such as bariatric surgery.

As far as cost containment, the English are clearly facing the same pressures as across the Atlantic, courtesy of the rapidly rising cost of technologies and medications. As there is an overall set budget established for the National Health Service (every three years), the inexorable march upward in cost is highly taxing on the system. In fact, even when optimistically factoring in projected improved efficiencies, a budget shortfall of $8.7 billion (USD) is still anticipated by 2020.(50)

This budget crunch cascades throughout medical services in the UK, including prescription drug costs. Like the US, these are expensive to the system overall. For the individual patients, via NHS, medication copays are typically low, at about $12.14 (USD) per prescription. In endeavoring to cap the associated expense to the nation, the UK has set up a body known as the National Institute of Health and Clinical Excellence (NICE). NICE's key role is to review and determine which treatments will become available to the populace. Once approved by this agency, then patients have covered access to such treatments, minus the copay. The opposite side of the coin, however, is that NICE has the authority to circumscribe both which medicines are and *are not* available under NHS coverage. There is understandably marked pressure to monitor expenditures, and NICE is acutely aware that "every pound spent on a new drug is potentially a pound not spent elsewhere... such as in general practice or in mental health services."(52) Therefore, while access may be broadly greater than Canada's system, there are still limits imposed on available medical therapies, even for a wealthy nation.

To expand on this point, oncology care really crystallizes how budgetary strains are growing year over year, with many therapies costing well in excess of $100,000 per year. Remember the leukemia drug, tisagenlecleucel, that carries a price tag of almost $500,000 for a course of treatment?(3) As a higher fraction of medicines come laden with stratospheric costs, NICE either simply cannot approve certain drugs for coverage under the NHS, or the money has to be taken away from another part of the budget. This again underscores that any nationalized health insurance system is inadequate in today's world of cutting-edge therapies, as governments simply cannot pay for everything for everyone. The funds have to come from somewhere. Furthermore, taking a bird's-eye view of England beyond medicine is the specter of Brexit, the decision by the United Kingdom to withdraw from the European Union after a referendum in June 2016. How the mechanics of Brexit function over the next several years (e.g., new trade contracts with different nations) will have major financial implications for England. Recall that, even in current conditions, there is a projected shortfall of $8.7 billion by 2020. Thus, British lawmakers will inevitably have to consider the entire calculus of all sectors of the economy in determining what funds are allocated to the NHS.

Where the rubber meets the road is when you consider, "What treatment does the patient in front of me need for her condition?" In the UK, the doctor's best medical recommendation may or may not be covered by NICE (if a prescription) or by NHS in general (e.g., fertility treatment has long wait times and is subject to strict criteria to qualify). To bypass these restrictions, there are an estimated 500 private hospitals and another 500 private office clinics across the UK.(50) Therefore, in the spirit of capitalism, if there is a need among consumers, and a service can be offered for a price, it is attainable. In this way, this is an example of a change that the UK realized was necessary due to the constraints and cost concerns detailed above. Private health insurance and private offices have led to enhanced access to care.

While this is a newer reform in the English system, approximately 5% of overall healthcare spending is on private options thus far, and it is rising.(50) It also bears noting that even within NHS services, some expense is apportioned to the patient. Dental treatment is a clear example, where per the NHS, patients will spend up to the equivalent of USD $300–400 *per course of treatment.* Equally telling is the measure of household spending on medical bills: this amounted to 14.8% of total expenditures in 2014.(50) Now consider the analogous measure for US households: according to the United States Department of Labor, in 2017 the average American household spent 8.2% of total expenditures on healthcare expenses!(53) You read that correctly—the fraction was *lower* for the US than the United Kingdom.

Therefore, the grass isn't always greener on the other side of the fence. In the United States, the system has created the need for the influx of foreign medical graduates. As a result of the factors driving US graduates away from primary care fields, and as citizens still require commensurate numbers of primary care physicians, doctors are immigrating to the United States to fill this need. However, regardless of national background, once in practice in America, there is no magical resilience shielding the International Graduate from the modern concoction of insurance denials, declining income, and dwindling time available per patient. Thereby, this concoction remains an accelerant in the recipe that conjures burnout. In fact, it is an intriguing paradox that while the foreign medical graduates who gain admittance have the top scores, the advantages theoretically conferred by this fund of medical knowledge is neutralized largely by the realities of practice. Academic brilliance will not aid you when the hospitalized patient cannot get transferred to a suitable nursing home on account of an insurance barrier.

Case Progress Update:
Dr. Madhava continues to follow up as an outpatient, now going on four months. Most of the conversations are philosophical and revolve around finding more meaning in her work. She often wonders aloud, "Can I really do this for the next 20 years?"

7

THE HOSPITAL-EMPLOYED DOCTOR

Dr. Jimmy Herbert is a 37-year-old gentleman who was admitted to our ward about eight weeks ago. He has been employed by a large university-affiliated hospital system for the past seven years but has become increasingly despondent. The nurse tells me that she has cared for him many times over the past few weeks and has often observed him watching cartoons on television—but has almost never heard him laugh. Review of his chart reveals that he checked himself in initially after complaining of feeling "trapped" in his job, with more pressures and criticisms thrown at him, and he felt an escape was the only recourse.

Those who knew Dr. Herbert in medical school describe him as a gregarious individual who loved to party. He wasn't known as being the hardest worker, but friends inform us that patients like his personality. Once he got through the rigors of residency, he felt that he had to get out and work. He wasn't motivated to subspecialize in cardiology or anything else— which would have required years of additional training. He wanted to "live life" and, when scouring job opportunities, recognized he wasn't truly interested in the business aspects of running a medical practice, so an employed position with a fixed schedule appealed to him greatly.

That was seven years ago. Over the past few years, he re-counts countless vital changes to his system-owned clinic. For one, literally none of the other doctors who were his associates in the clinic are still here today. They all moved on to other jobs after a few years. Jimmy notes a palpable ambiance of transience in the office: any of the doctors, nurses, or medical assistants could resign tomorrow, and no one would be surprised at this point. The clinic remains housed in a beautiful modern office building, with the hardwood floors always polished and assuredly sterile. But while he would never describe himself as an idealist, and though patients continue to come through the glass doors, without a doubt this turnover has been noticeably disruptive for patients.

Worse than that, the patient scheduling now allows "over-books" without the doctor's permission—so more than one patient is scheduled for a specific time. Apparently, management felt that more patients had to be seen to make up for the financial impact of staff turnover and recruitment. Dr. Herbert has always been a guy who wanted to take the occasional coffee break and chill a little—and that's part of why he wanted an employed 9-5 type of position. Moreover, he and his other physician associates grumble that the administrators never asked their opinion about the schedule whatsoever. Adding insult to injury, about three months prior to his admission, someone in the clinic—he does not know who—complained to an administrator about his patients waiting too long. He subsequently got a phone call from a hospital system administrator who led off by asking confrontationally, "So what's the problem?" and the remainder of the conversation was loaded with criticism, repeating twice that "you know we do patient satisfaction surveys."

He has been similarly agape at the automated messages he gets from his EMR every Monday morning upon logging in that tell him he spends 24 minutes per patient, followed by "tips" to cut down the "time per patient." In a twisted version of artificial intelligence, one of these supremely helpful suggestions includes typing his note while the patient is in the room talking. This triggered an instant response, with Dr. Herbert thinking, "Wait a minute—I'm a 'people person'—I hate computers! And now I won't even be looking at my patient for 90% of the visit?"

These experiences have led to a distinct disconcerting sense that his whole work structure is setting him up for failure. He has seen other doctors come and go and has pondered whether he is being a fool by sticking around, while becoming increasingly irritated by clinic operations. He doesn't know what to do next and has felt increasingly paralyzed. Now in our ward, he is barely talking. His medical school classmates would barely recognize his personality.

***

We have discussed at length the forces driving declining reimbursements to physicians and shorter time available with patients. However, for a doctor, there is something that can rival dissatisfaction with remuneration: respect. While physicians in the United States have been fortunate to have enjoyed a strong income level for years, another key attribute melded with a career in medicine is that the occupation carries with it a high degree of esteem. A common adjective linked to a medical career is "noble", as after all, doctors often have the lives of their patients in their hands (and minds). In this vein, there is a term that has come into routine usage in the medical field that truly is a headwind to the respect associated with doctors; that word is "provider." For those who are unfamiliar, provider is short for "healthcare provider", and effectively lumps numerous professionals who encounter patients into this generic term. And with all due respect to my nonphysician healthcare workers, whom I work with and admire greatly in active medical practice, "provider" is dramatically denigrating to doctors.

Many physicians will have a viscerally negative response to being labeled a provider. We are not simply technicians doling out bits and pieces of healthcare. We are highly educated individuals who have spent years in rigorous training to then competently shoulder the enormous burden of another human being's life. In my own subspecialization of oncology, I acutely see this all the time: patients facing cancer, placing tremendous trust and hope in my abilities to successfully battle this killer scourge. On even my most cynical days I can sense the pulsating feeling of this responsibility. In the tale of *Homo sapiens*, very little matters in the way that life and death do.

However, in large hospital-operated clinics, there is a wholly different plane of concern. Their task is with issues such as staffing and how many "providers" are manning a given clinic or hospital unit. As long as these various employees can bill the patient and thereby generate money for the system, who cares whether the individual is a neurosurgeon from Harvard with 20 years of experience and 50 scientific publications, a nurse practitioner two years out of school, or anyone else? In a hypothetical hospital-owned cardiology clinic, they may need 10 providers to see the 200 patients coming into their expensive building today. At the end of the day, these are merely soldiers on the ground generating money for the hospital. Therefore, the provider is simply a cog in the proverbial machine.

The core maladaptation of the hospital-employed physician is similar to the idealistic physician, as these employed docs have little recourse but to work hard and see patients. They don't have a say in the mechanics of clinic functions. However, there is a crucial compounding characteristic: without decision-making power and lack of respect, the risk of apathy in one's daily work is much higher than that of the idealistic physician, as well as lack of loyalty to the organization.

Think about any skilled professional job: if you do not have material input into daily operations, and the boss doesn't value your efforts, how will you feel? Particularly as there is no lack of physician job opportunities across the nation? Doctors are used to working hard, but that effort will not get you far in this construct. While individual contracts can vary, hospital-employed positions typically are salaried positions, sometimes coupled with a bonus structure that may or may not be realistically attainable. Imagine the feeling of resignation when as a doctor, you are rounding late into the evening or night at the hospital, and this at best yields minor tangible financial benefits. Akin to our patient Dr. Herbert, it is exceedingly uncommon to get any credit—even lip service—for working late into the night. These doctors likely only get a phone call from the administrators when there is a problem. In this world of faceless providers staffing clinics, it is truly a punitive culture of disrespect.

In large systems, middle management can further compound the problem. These individuals are frequently tasked with monitoring or enforcing system policies. When the physician is already dealing with a culture of disrespect, interactions with those who are pushing the policies aligned with the maligned system will have a low threshold for devolving into a clash. The middle manager may not necessarily be doing this with any malicious intent, of course, but there is surely that subset that more overzealously pursues their responsibilities.

This latter circumstance is when rules are adhered to, such that all practicality is thrown out the window. For example, one of my old classmates from training, now working as a hematologist for a hospital clinic, was told that no laboratory orders can be entered by anyone other than a physician. This extended to even the most basic of blood tests for a hematologist, known as the complete blood count, or CBC. This absurd "rule" caused the following to occur on a regular basis: a patient is added on to the schedule unbeknownst to the physician. This patient is then waiting at the lab, at which point the middle manager comes to the physician and pointedly says something to the effect of "Mr. Smith has been waiting for 10 minutes and needs an order." Then the physician, in the midst of seeing complicated cases, and after recovering from his appalled reaction, must go to his or her computer, find a different patient's chart, enter, and sign the order. My colleague notes that when he experiences this interruption, it is highly distracting to his train of thought, and he is incredibly concerned about the risk of medical error (e.g., wrong patient chart or lab order selected).

Even higher up the mountain of absurdity is that a nurse—regardless of how experienced—is not allowed to enter this most basic of hematology lab tests for the waiting patient. My physician colleague laughed incredulously when relating this example to me, saying, "I'm confident my nurse with 18 years of hematology experience has the requisite training to enter a CBC order." We both laughed; it would be funnier if it wasn't true. Echoing the physician's comments, there is a real risk for medical error.

This doctor, along with his associates, brought this up to the administration, seeking some kind of reasonable compromise, such as having a core set of tests that can be ordered if the physician is busy with a patient. However, this was promptly vetoed without any reasonable discussion. Moreover, the person who rejected the compromise proposal was a middle manager physician. That's right—a physician who is placed in this role, and functions in the tight confines of being a pawn of the system.

Physicians in this position are not the chairman of the department but simply propped up (often with very few if any scientific publications) to keep physicians "in line" with the system policies, however misguided they may be. Not shockingly, these doctors have minimal genuine interest in constructive feedback. Of course, there are positive exceptions, but there are eerily similar stories throughout the country.

In a very illuminating book, *The 5 Levels of Leadership*, author John Maxwell called this the "lowest level of leadership."(42) You have to listen to these middle managers, not because they have any charisma, character, leadership skills, or credentials, but rather, purely because they have been propped into such a position. Maxwell perceptively notes that these individuals "may be bosses, but they are never leaders... They rely on rules, regulations, policies, and organization charts to control people." Hence, under such a structure, when the employees don't feel valued and are following policies simply because they have limited or no choice, there is a limit to how much effort they will put into their work.

Maxwell is also quite prescient in discussing the difficulties of such low-level bosses. He comments on the strain such people have in dealing with the highly educated, such as physicians. These bosses are further exposed in the eyes of the highly educated, because physicians know full well that this low level of leadership "does not require ability and effort to achieve. Anyone can be appointed to a 'position.'"(42) Thus, the physician placed in such a role, who does not enjoy respect in his field or have scientific publications behind his name, falls into this poor choice of a boss perfectly.

Now there has been much research in both classical economics and psychology over the years, examining the relationship of appreciation and dedication to one's job. Two prominent experiments illustrating this were conducted by Dr. Dan Ariely, professor of Psychology and Behavioral Economics at Duke University.(28) In the first one, two groups of participants were tasked with building complex Lego robot figures. There were two key elements in the study: one was that participants were compensated with gradually less money for each subsequent robot made—and therefore diminishing financial rewards. The second was that for one group, all Lego models were stored until the very end of the entire experiment (i.e., after all block figures were constructed) and in the other, each robot was disassembled immediately after creation. The deconstruction was carried out by those conducting the study, right before the eyes of the participants.

The results of this study are fascinating: the group whose robots were preserved intact until the very end of the study built 57% more Lego creations than the other group. Therefore, both groups were paid the same for each robot, but there is an apparent potent psychological impact of seeing your work actively destroyed immediately after your effort to complete the task. This has clear parallels to efforts at one's job in general: if after all your hard work, you are receiving no appreciation—regardless of money—and perhaps your efforts are being actively neutralized or ignored, then the motivation to persevere in your job will ultimately decrease. It's the "Why even bother?" feeling, throwing your hands up.

Upon reading this study, this reminded me of a patient case mentioned to me by one of my long-time colleagues in a different state in the US who had been working as an employed doctor for a system. A complicated patient with colorectal cancer presented to him for consultation. This patient had strong personal beliefs for refusing traditional Western treatment such as chemotherapy and radiation. The radiation oncologist and medical oncologist spent literally hours discussing the rationale, benefits, and risks of treatment approaches and did their best to search for treatments that were outside the box but still medically reasonable. Then, suddenly, the radiation oncologist's manager (who was a physician, by the way), once he heard of this situation, without either informing the physicians or requesting any input, transferred the patient's care to a different radiation and medical oncologist. Needless to say, the doctors were totally stunned. There was absolutely no appreciation of the hours of high-complexity effort both in the outpatient clinics and the hospital, and it culminated with the patient's care being switched without even the courtesy of a phone call. In practicing medicine over 20 years each, they felt this was the height of unprofessionalism for a physician to usurp someone's patient in this manner. Therefore, one can understand the immediate thought, "Why bother, when surrounded by individuals like these who have no hesitation in being callously unprofessional?" Analogous to the

Lego robot experiment, when one's work is being destroyed and totally unappreciated in this manner, the motivation to persevere sharply decreases.

Dr. Ariely's second experiment is a fascinating corollary to the prior experiment. In this study, participants had to identify pairs of identical letters among a series of random letters printed on paper.(28) There were three groups: one group circled their answers and wrote their name with the submission, and this was then acknowledged by the experimenter. The second cohort did not write their names with their answers, and the third cohort had the paper with their answers shredded after handing it to the experimenter for review. All groups were offered more money if more of these puzzles were completed.

The outcome is quite intriguing. Those whose papers were ripped up required *double* the compensation as those whose work was acknowledged in order to keep doing the task! Extrapolating to the real world, common sense tells us that employers are obviously not going to double your salary to put up with their underappreciation.

We see macro-level evidence of this also, as across a breadth of industries since the economic recovery stemming from the financial events of 2008, wage growth has been overall minimal. Although the broader domestic stock market has done extremely well, with corporate profits up handsomely in multiple sectors and unemployment at its lowest level in decades (under 4% in 2018), average workers have not seen commensurate pay increases. Thus, while in theory, employers provide raises to retain staff, this is not happening in reality.(29)

So if administrators are not interested in doling out appreciation for the hard work of clinicians, what do they care about? In addition to dollars flowing into the system, the answer to this question is an eye-opener: patient satisfaction surveys! Now don't get me wrong, I definitely care about patient satisfaction in a general sense, but the details of these surveys will strike many readers as shocking. Fundamentally, why does anyone care about survey results? The answer is two-fold: money and money. More specifically, firstly, this is publicity for a facility like a hospital to draw greater numbers of patients into their system to generate money. The second is that, since a few years ago, the administrators at the Department of Health and Human Services decided to link survey scores as 25% of a hospital's "value-based purchasing score," which directly impacts receipt of Medicare reimbursement.(30) The advent of the Affordable Care Act (ACA) layered the wrinkle of having 2% of total Medicare reimbursements *held* from hospitals and those with the highest scores "earning" that money back. Thus, one can clearly see the powerful motivation of fixating on maximizing survey scores, just as the administrator told our fictional Dr. Herbert.

Patient survey answers are problematic for many reasons, and this is magnified when millions of dollars are at stake. In the game of trying to maximize positive survey results, and consequently gain Medicare dollars, there are professional groups that search for statistical correlations so as to learn where the primary focus of improving the patient "experience" should be. An excellent example, while from a Canadian organization, is very indicative of what happens across America as well. In researching the top five associations that will improve scores, they found that the most likely factor leading to a patient bestowing the highest possible rating to a hospital is the "quality of the food"; in fact, perceived food quality had a four-fold link with achievement of the highest score.(31) The remainder of the top five statistical findings are: cleanliness of the room and bathroom, whether the nurse "always" listened to the patient, belief that the local health region takes safety in the hospital seriously, and the hospital staff "always" did "everything they could" to help with their pain. (See Table 1.)

Top Variables Influencing Satisfaction	
1	Quality of the Food
2	Cleanliness of the Room
3	Did the nurse "always" listen to the patient?
4	Perception that hospital safety is taken seriously
5	Hospital Staff "always" did "everything they could" to help with pain

Table 1. The five leading variables influencing patient satisfaction survey results for hospitals.

Even having seen crazy survey questions for several years, I was taken aback by these correlations. Striking is that none of the top five findings mention the physician, nor anything related to the patient's primary medical ailment getting better. Therefore, the message is that, to a degree, doctors are interchangeable: as long as someone is there to see the patients, enter orders, and bill on behalf of the hospital, that is all that practically matters. Is it any wonder that the derisive label "provider" is used nowadays? Furthermore, note the emphasis that was found related to pain control—and the perception of "always" doing everything possible to help with pain. Ponder that for a moment: pain control is therefore more strongly linked with the highest hospital scores rather than something like "I felt my condition was being treated well." With millions of dollars at stake (as scores are a critical part of getting more Medicare dollars), it should be no surprise that pain score assessments are nowadays both ubiquitous and mandatory on nursing shifts in most hospitals across the country. This has further led to hospital-employed palliative care teams being deployed in many locations. In fact, some hospitalist physicians even have "Palliative Care consultation" on their daily rounding checklist. From a medical necessity perspective, this is truly laughable. (*Remember: you may also get charged those increased hospital rates for that consultation along with for any medications they recommend.*) However, I am confident that with these teams roving through the hospital wards "always doing everything they can" to alleviate physical discomfort, hospital scores are going nicely upward. Obviously patient outcomes matter foremost to a physician, but these confusing signals for healthcare staff (doctors, nurses, etc.) can cloud one's sense of priorities during the workday. The nurse may feel, "Should I follow up with the surgical team to clarify the operative plans or make sure I have the required pain scores completed and the pain medications dispensed to the patient?"

Predictably, a number of societies have been quite critical of these hospital surveys. These include Emergency Medicine groups, which have shed light onto several problematic aspects of surveys.(32) Firstly, sample size of respondents can lead to misleading results and thereby misguided priorities. For example, Press Ganey Associates, which partners with roughly 40% of hospitals, has claimed that at least 30 surveys are needed to draw "meaningful" conclusions.

However, even when less than this threshold has been met, responses are analyzed, and hospitals are placed into percentiles reaped from these results. Consequently, some emergency medicine departments have had wild fluctuations in their rankings. If the data bear questionable validity, it is highly concerning that enormous sums of money are distributed when some departments do not have a large enough sample size. But this is unquestionably a chief focus for organizations. As a publication in the *Cleveland Clinic Journal of Medicine* phrased it, "The consumer-centric shift of healthcare has moved patient attitudes, preferences, and experience to the top of the list of priorities for healthcare organizations."(66)

It appears there is also a striking benefit to the patient encounter with the ensuing quick, tidy conclusion rather than the serious case that is life-threatening. For emergency medicine physicians or trauma surgeons, if substantial time is spent saving a patient's life, other patients who are waiting as a result may furnish lower satisfaction scores (and this definitely happens in actuality). This scenario can manifest anywhere in the country. Akin to our Dr. Herbert, who faced veiled threats about patient satisfaction scores potentially affecting his employment standing, this atmosphere can lead to a true conflict of interest: that is, it is advantageous for job security to quickly discharge patients than to spend time performing a detailed workup into a disquieting patient complaint. Also recall the dynamic on a separate level, where the hospital will be aligned with the same conflict of interest on rapid patient discharges as the system strives to maximize survey results that beget greater monies into their coffers.

A report by the Hastings Center, a nonpartisan research institution dedicated to bioethics, found other "unintended consequences" of patient satisfaction surveys as well.(33)

For one, the authors postulated that placing a misguided weight to patient satisfaction could result in a greater portion of medically unnecessary tests and procedures. This leads to a second finding, which is that costs get driven upward as a consequence.

This notion linking satisfaction to higher costs has been borne out in the real world also. A study published in the *Archives of Internal Medicine* examined data associated with nearly 52,000 survey respondents, and after adjusting for a number of confounding variables such as medical insurance, health status, and demographics (e.g., age), a few astounding findings were reported.(34) The quartile of patients with the highest satisfaction had excess cost of care, by 8.8% (compared to the "least satisfied" quartile), 9.1% more prescription medicine expenses, and most shockingly, 26% relative higher mortality (specifically, the hazard ratio was 1.26 for higher mortality risk, with the 95% confidence interval ranging from 1.05 to 1.53). Think about that—in data from 52,000 patients over several years, the most "satisfied" also died more often! This study had the highly apropos title, "The Cost of Satisfaction."

On the contrary to the negative consequences of satisfaction surveys, I posit that proper treatment by a physician is grounded in giving the best medical recommendation regardless of patient happiness. In this vein, the Hastings Center report mentioned earlier also appealed for greater courage among healthcare professionals to look beyond patient satisfaction and rather do the right thing medically for the patient. After all, if your loved one needed urgent cardiac bypass surgery to prevent a heart attack, do you want to hear the raw truth or a sugar-coated "Oh sure, he can enjoy golf tomorrow with his buddies first!"?

Taken together, these circumstances lead to the maladaptations of the system-employed doctor. As you can see, in the toxic brew of underappreciation, criticism from middle managers, relatively limited financial reward for working beyond the minimum, and administrators' priorities lying in matters such as surveys, the natural outcome is erosion of both loyalty and motivation.

An encounter I faced with a hospital-employed infectious disease doctor a few years ago astonishingly exemplifies this maladaptation. As a hematologist, I was consulted for a patient developing acute anemia—low red blood cell count. Anemia can lead to a host of medical effects, including fatigue, shortness of breath, and cardiovascular stress. In my field of blood medicine, we often act akin to detectives, piecing together a timeline of events and generating hypotheses to explain a medical conundrum. My assessment revealed two key issues: first, that the drop was a very rapid one, which typically only occurs secondary to two possible etiologies, and second, that there was a clear temporal relationship to the start of an antibiotic treatment, namely ceftriaxone. Now it is well-known in the general public that antibiotics carry a plethora of side effect risks, many of which are gastrointestinal or allergic in nature. Ceftriaxone has another grave adverse association: that of hemolytic anemia. In this condition, also known as hemolysis, red blood cells are being destroyed. This cell lysis can result from a few different mechanisms, and for ceftriaxone, a potent antibody can form that attacks certain proteins on the surface of red blood cells. Although a relatively rare side effect, it can be life-threatening. For instance, one potential complication of severe acute anemia is a heart attack. Published studies support that there is a high mortality risk with ceftriaxone-induced hemolysis.

In my patient's lab work, he had multiple signs of hemolysis occurring, including the finding of a high potassium concentration in the blood stream. On account of my concern of a link to the antibiotic, I contacted the infectious disease physician to directly discuss the case. With the high risk of death, I paged the other doctor as soon as I thought of this; I attempted to reach him around 6:15 p.m., and again about 30 minutes later when I had not received a return phone call on my mobile phone.

Now, bear in mind that a high potassium level can sometimes be extreme enough to land a person in the hospital. The infectious disease doctor finally called me back. After the initial pleasantries in speaking with a colleague I had never met previously, I detailed my concerns. Tactfully, I asked him if he saw that the lab results he had personally ordered revealed a potassium level of over 6, which is life-threatening. Incredibly, he simply replied with a one-liner reeking of insouciance, "Yeah, I saw that it was a little high." As his voice trailed off, I replied directly, "Look, it's more than a 'little high'; it's over 6. I don't know if you normally have an assistant review lab results for you, but this is highly concerning. I'm worried the ceftriaxone the patient is currently receiving is causing hemolytic anemia." He still was not animated in the slightest. He gave some noncommittal response, essentially signaling that he was not that interested in the issue. As he obviously was not going to address this problem, being that it was already after normal working hours, and as stabilizing a high potassium is not in my area of expertise, I had no choice but to recommend the patient go to the emergency department.

This episode happened over five years ago, but it irritates me to this day. It clearly fails the basic litmus test of "What would you do if it was your mother?" Moreover, I keep wondering what was going through the infectious disease doctor's mind to be so unwilling to help the patient. Two crucial points are that he was the doctor prescribing the antibiotic, and secondly, he had himself ordered the lab test that showed the critically high potassium value. Was he just a bad doctor? Or simply uncaring?

Well, layering this issue with the concept of the maladaptations of the employed physician, I hypothesize that he once may have been more caring and willing to take immediate and appropriate action—particularly if another physician called him after office hours to directly discuss a case. However, after years of operating within a system that does not reward going the extra mile for a patient, not receiving adequate appreciation, and being a salaried employee, his own behavior may have maladapted to the pernicious system such that it affected his job performance. In other words, I surmise this was a symptom of burnout! Not feeling valued ultimately manifests in other ways, such as cavalier responses toward concerned colleagues. In contrast, receiving a phone call like this after hours more typically has a physician "peer pressure" effect, where one feels obligated to take action out of avoiding professional embarrassment, for starters.

This dovetails into our recurring theme of physician burnout. A survey conducted of 3,700 US physicians in 2018, known as the Physician Workload Survey, discovered that 52% of doctors feel "regularly" burned out.(35) That is an absolutely huge number. The specific percentage naturally varied by specialty and spanned 44–58%. Now, akin to the encounter with the infectious disease doctor, this study determined that 45–57% of the participants felt that burnout "affected performance" at work. In the obvious context of a human being's health or life at stake, this naturally has potentially serious repercussions.

Another recent report investigating this very issue was the Medscape Physicians Lifestyle Report.(36) They unearthed that the top three factors contributing to burnout are too many bureaucratic tasks, too many hours, and feeling like a "cog in the wheel." Therefore, putting it together, consider that over half of physicians feel regularly burned out, and approximately half of these individuals admitted their job performance suffered as a result. Fellow citizens, you should be highly alarmed!

Is it any wonder that these underappreciated "providers"—expected to run on the treadmill through as many patients as possible every day to generate revenue for the system, while they are largely on a fixed salary—have a high turnover? It stands to reason that, naturally, doctors will simply change jobs once they get sick of all the flaws in a given position. Fortunately, there is still one feature of the profession that remains on the positive side of the ledger for doctors: there are plenty of jobs available in the country, especially if one is flexible about moving.

Now please bear in mind these are generalizations and observations of trends; I want to be very clear on that perspective. There are, of course, many outstanding exceptions of both hospitals and employed doctors. But I can tell you that, in interviewing dozens of physician colleagues, these scenarios are disconcertingly common. Analogous to my experience with an infectious disease physician, I do not propose that the individuals themselves are intentionally embracing suboptimal traits. Rather, they have maladapted due to the multitude of forces detailed in our discussion.

Going into medicine for the vast majority is *not* about money. If you are doing it for money, and not enjoyment of healing patients, you will quickly be miserable from the grind, the years of schooling, and the medical school loans you pay off over years. But being rewarded financially by an employer in a salaried position does reflect respect and appreciation for your dedication and hard work, to some extent. And when that does not occur, lack of motivation is a very natural course of action. The undervalued doctor with diminished motivation may think, "Why should I round on that extra patient in the hospital when no one wants to appreciate my effort? Screw it—I'm going home and enjoying my time off."

Case Progress Update:
Dr. Herbert was recently seen saying a few words intermittently. The nurse observed him surfing the internet, and it appeared he was setting up a fantasy football team. The cartoons have still been playing on the television.

8

THE WEALTHY DOCTOR

For this next patient, we'll be making a house call. Or more specifically, to a local sports bar. Meet Dr. Ozzie Phillips, sitting near the center of the bar. That's right, the middle-aged man with the sharp blue sport coat and the youthful hair. But you wouldn't know it from his old med school ID picture; "floppy hair" and "lab rat" were the most apt phrases for him back then, when he thought of himself foremost as a burgeoning researcher. Today, however, he's catching up with a colleague over a beer after work, watching the NFL playoffs. After complaining about work for a bit, his friend says after a sip, leaning in, "But hey, I've been meaning to tell you, you really should think of doing aesthetics. It's totally changed the complexion of my day. I even hired an extra front desk person and I get home earlier. Part of me just can't believe people are paying for this stuff! I mean, you hear about it, but I thought that was Beverly Hills or something." Dr. Phillips soaked it all in, like in the afterglow of an epiphany.

Fast forward six months. He took his old buddy's advice, and after the initial learning curve, Dr. Phillips has increased revenues by over 25% per month with the aesthetic services in his office. He remarked, "Who knew techie types from the local large corporations were into this stuff? And some have started bringing their mothers and significant others too.

That's right, it's not 'just the women'." He always had an intuitive brilliance, and quickly realized he could do more and more of these cosmetic services. Why deal with insurance appeals, enormous amounts of time clicking in an EMR, when you can partake in such a financial windfall?

So why are we seeing Dr. Phillips on our ward rounds? Well, he sought our services because of a more philosophical conundrum. He simply can't shake the feeling at times that this isn't "real medicine." He's increasingly ceasing his clinical and research work. But long-time patients have remarked to him that Dr. Phillips is "looking less stressed"! And that's without giving himself any Botox injections.

***

B otox, antiaging creams, men's "vitality centers," and fad diet advice are commonplace nowadays. The revolutionary part of this wave is that many doctors themselves are either heavily incorporating these services into their daily practices, or have entirely dedicated themselves to it. This belies the humble scientific origins of botulinum toxin, as "Botox" is properly known, in the 19th century. During his investigation of food poisoning, Dr. Justinus Kerner in Germany studied what was occurring in those dying from food poisoning upon consuming sausage (with the condition later dubbed "botulism"). Suspecting a substance within the food leading to the devastating symptoms, he even injected himself with samples of poisoned food; such direct investigation was routinely practiced at that time among physicians and chemists. He fortunately did not contract the most deadly form of botulism but, through his work, carefully described the hallmark signs of the condition.

Nowadays, you see clinics that give Botox and similar cosmetic treatments all over the country. The market size for such therapies is absolutely huge, reported to be in the range of $4.5 to $15 billion in 2018. (4, 62) Dr. Phillips's colleague expressed surprise that people "are paying for this stuff," but he shouldn't be. Consider the fundamental idea that such treatments symbolize: the fountain of youth. This phrase attained significant prominence in world culture by way of the efforts of the Spanish conquistador Ponce de Leon, who was searching for the eponymous fountain in Florida in the 16th century. But the search has not ended. Although literally superficial, the appeal of being able to be draped in youthful-looking skin for a few hundred dollars is irresistible for many, as evidenced by the revenue reaching into the billions.

Analogous to this is another market alluded to by the men's "vitality centers". These clinics are largely involved with testosterone replacement therapy to address hypogonadism—or testosterone deficiency—in men. The large-scale marketing is impressive. Led by the labeling of the testosterone deficiency as "low T" (I can assure you this is not an actual medical term!), and with advertising regularly featuring men who are pumping iron in the gym or catching football passes in the endzone, this too has successfully created a huge market. The Global Testosterone Replacement Therapy Market Report, an analysis conducted with data available from 2013—2017, estimates that the United States market is approximately $1.8 billion in 2019.(63) Intriguingly, the largest market share globally is that of the United States, to the tune of 86% of the market for testosterone replacement therapy.

While a botulinum toxin injection is purely cosmetic (getting older with the associated skin changes is *not* a medical disease), the data for testosterone replacement is far from robust. An editorial by authors from Georgetown University in Washington, DC, published in 2017 through The American Association of Family Physicians (AAFP) stated, "Although some off-label medication use is justified, the use of testosterone for nonspecific symptoms of aging is not." The authors went on to comment that treating symptoms of natural human aging such as "decreased energy, decreased strength, low libido, erectile dysfunction, mood disorders, sleep disorders, or poor memory is inappropriate because symptoms do not correlate with testosterone levels."(69) They further dissected the published medical literature, as well as the data for side effects of inappropriate testosterone usage. The adverse consequences include risk of prostate cancer (as testosterone is a stimulant to the prostate gland as well as prostate cancer cells) and potentially cardiovascular disease. The time-honored adage in medicine is *primum non nocere,* meaning in Latin "first, do no harm." Therefore, logic dictates that if there is the possibility of harm to the patient without a sound foundation of benefit, then do not experiment with the patient's health!

Furthermore, there are a list of conditions that can cause low testosterone, including diabetes, steroid medication usage, and obesity. As men age, testosterone levels also fall about 1–2% per year.(70) In other words, low testosterone is not the *disease*, but merely a symptom of another condition. That is a critical distinction medically. As noted in an article by Harvard Health Publishing in 2016, "if you do not have any key symptoms, especially fatigue and sexual dysfunction, which are the most common, it is not recommended you go on [testosterone] therapy given the uncertainty about long-term safety."(70)

The accretion of these types of medical therapies, entwined with the huge market (such as the $15 billion botulinum toxin market size), have created a burgeoning opportunity for those motivated to depart from traditional evidence-based medicine due to insurance pressures and the like. Again, there are many people who want and seek these services. To deliver these services, it typically requires a medical degree in the United States (e.g., for legal prescription) and properly weighing the pros and cons of a procedure for a given patient, but it ultimately does not require deep thought.

Physicians who have melded procedures like botulinum toxin into their daily practices are often doing so to obtain another revenue stream and, thereby, keep the rest of their practice afloat, maintain a certain income level, and escape medical insurance headaches (the latter avoided as patients generally pay out of pocket for cosmetic services). Furthermore, if you interview these physicians, almost none will say they were motivated to go through years of study and the rigor of medical school so they could one day give Botox shots. To give you a flavor of more typical backgrounds, I have personally interviewed numerous impressive students who have scoured opportunities to obtain laboratory research positions or volunteer their time in rural clinics in Africa. Now, these doctors who are injecting botulinum toxin to attempt to pause the inexorable march of time are often (but not always) dermatologists and plastic surgeons. This latter detail is further absurd to me as a physician, as these are specialties that are hypercompetitive to enter! This contingent of medical students had to have top grades, glittering recommendations, and research publications; now they are reduced to administering simple shots and fillers, no diagnostic brilliance required! Isn't it sad that this situation exists, and we have an insurance reimbursement system that you cannot get paid enough via normal patient care? Therefore, in effect, this is a brain drain, where the best minds are not engaged in patient care of those who are facing challenging diseases and treatments. There is no doubt that this is a loss for the healthcare of the public.

Now, I mention that not all medical practitioners who engage in these cosmetic-style therapies are necessarily dermatologists or plastic surgeons. Not surprisingly, with the aforementioned market opportunity in conjunction with the woefully poor status quo, other doctors are aspiring for their piece of the pie. For instance, a few primary care practices I have shared patients with in North Carolina offer myriad aesthetic services in addition to traditional medical consultations. Patients often enter a separate area of the practice for these services and then review their cosmetic concerns with a beautician. She then provides recommendations that may include antiaging creams and fillers, depending on the patient's specific concerns. These options are typically not covered by medical insurance, but patients are willing to pay cash to sip from the fountain of youth.

Doctors are now even openly advertising for these cosmetic therapies, which at one time were deemed unseemly for the profession. One that I came across had the smiling picture and name of the physician, with the generic title "Board Certified Physician, M.D." The marketing blurb stated that this particular clinic was "one of the first centers to introduce Jeuveau (a neurotoxin similar to botulinum toxin) and is now FDA-approved and available to patients." The bird's-eye view of this is also that the broader global cosmetics industry is glamorously successful, to the tune of roughly $300 to $500 billion, additionally supporting the premise that people are willing to pay for their physical appearance and youthfulness. (64, 65)

Put together, this is a maladaptation that these talented physicians are both literally and figuratively engaging in superficial medical pursuits like botulinum toxin shots in order to escape the insurance system and stabilize their income. Their collective brilliance and years of experience are wasted on the mundane. And this group is expanding, fueled by the insurance climate and other systemic problems in medicine. Isn't this a loss for the general public? I would argue wholeheartedly that it is.

The fact that some primary care practices offer aesthetic services makes complete sense to me. While the public may hear vaguely about lifestyle, hours, and income differences among physicians, the reality is that the primary care physician in America faces the dual pressure of comparatively lower salaries than plastic surgeons and dermatologists, and the inextricable insurance crunch to their daily practice. On top of this is the 50% of the workday clicking within the EHR system! Many physicians lament even taking a vacation because upon returning to the office, there are scores of messages from insurance companies denying a patient coverage for a medication or stacks of paperwork. For instance, an orthopedic colleague posted a picture on the professional networking app, LinkedIn, of the dozens of forms that were on his desk when he returned from vacation. The accompanying comment was "Returned home from vacation to find a pile of ... forms so that our broken system can continue to function in an inefficient and wasteful manner. It would take hours away from meaningful clinical care and family." The last sentence conveys insight to the surgeon's personal priorities as well: "clinical care" and "family". Both of these are naturally quite reasonable and commonplace, and they hit on the essence of the work-life balance. If the highly trained orthopedic surgeon is going to work, he wishes to engage in "meaningful clinical care" and not hours spent with paperwork and electronic health record systems. Since he cannot singlehandedly transform the system, he has the choice of either putting up with it or making a fundamental change to his daily work, such as the botulinum toxin concept.

Another telling example is from one of my own patients, who was on a medication for low blood counts (conferring a higher risk for bleeding) for over a year, for which a medical insurance company abruptly denied coverage of this pill upon the patient switching to a new plan. The medication is approved by the US Food and Drug Administration (FDA), based on Phase III randomized clinical trials (considered the strongest level of evidence) published in medical journals. The patient has been clinically stable and responding to the treatment, with fortunately minimal side effects. Furthermore, suddenly stopping a needed medication is, quite frankly, dangerous for the patient. For the well-being of my patient to remain stable, my office staff and I had to make numerous phone calls to both the health insurance company and to the manufacturer of the medication, send a number of faxes and forms with medical documentation, and write a letter appealing the case with the insurance company. Consider, that all of this effort was simply to maintain the status quo—so my patient could remain on his current effective, data-driven FDA-approved therapy! In spite of the abject absurdity of it all, doctors will do this for the sake of their patient. However, it is lost on no one that this time expended generated no revenue whatsoever for the doctor or their organization.

These real-world examples stunningly occur multiple times per week in practices across the nation. If doctors stay within traditional medical practice, they have no choice but to battle the insurance companies (again, this is completely *nonreimbursed* time) and see more patients in the less remaining time to maintain their income. Is it any wonder that the thought of abjuring clinical practice and transitioning to one buttressed by botulinum toxin shots shimmers like a yellow brick road?

Another lucrative nontraditional option by which physicians can renovate their practice is by looking above this yellow brick road, and to the stars. That is, they can find a niche as a doctor to the stars or a similar celebrity route. To be successful in such a niche, however, the doctor must possess the right attributes: well-spoken, magnetic personality, and having the right "look". Working with famous clients clearly helps too. There are a number of successful examples of this. Competitive professional athletes, for instance, essentially have a list of international go-to surgeons when one suffers a serious injury. Beyond being known to athletes, select orthopedic surgeons and sports medicine specialists are on the virtual Rolodex of prominent sports clubs everywhere. National Football League teams will even keep these doctors on their staff to promptly protect their valuable athletes. With experience, and working with world famous athletes who may subsequently sing the surgeon's praises, these physicians develop glittering (and deserved) reputations.

Along this journey to work with high-profile athletes, some of these doctors can even make the seminal transition away from routine orthopedic practice. If executed well, they may never look back at traditional practice. After all, any highly trained doctor, particularly if also a sports fan, will understandably find this nontraditional path immensely satisfying, liberated from the world of billing, paperwork, and EHRs, and probably also quintessentially cool.

Another shining avenue of leveraging one's medical degree and commensurate experience is being on television. You've seen these physicians on both local and national channels; a shining example is Dr. Sanjay Gupta, who has been the chief medical correspondent on CNN for years.(71) In addition, there is a cavalcade of physicians who will be contacted by local news networks to comment on a contemporary topic in disciplines such as cardiology, dermatology, and cancer research.

Being on television has a multitude of benefits for the physician. For one, being labeled an expert on TV confers respect and generally good publicity. People may recognize you at restaurants around town and inflate your social standing, whether you desire this or not. Moreover, this can translate into augmented demand for the doctor's medical opinion. Patients will be motivated to self-refer to the local celebrity doctor, and the nearby medical community will know your name more readily as well. In the vein of some of the issues we have discussed, such as those pertaining to large hospital systems, most doctors greatly value the gain in respect. In the mindset of doctors, when you are working assiduously to apply highly specialized medical knowledge to improve the health of another person, you sincerely hope for a certain degree of respect and appreciation. This is an instructive distinction: in the long run, to be paid well but disrespected is not acceptable for most doctors, just as it is not acceptable for most people in general.

However, not simply anyone can fit this role of a doctor on TV. You've seen news anchors: they have to be physically attractive or appear distinguished and furthermore possess a proper speaking voice for such a position. One has to have a reasonable fashion sense and often have a good sense of humor, as well as social skills, to play well on television. Akin to an athletic injury expert, the average doctor cannot simply decide to engage in this nontraditional role of being a medical expert on the news. This aforementioned set of attributes is as much a prerequisite as are their medical credentials.

It is worth briefly delving into some of the proposals in the healthcare conversation in current times, such as that of a single-payer system in the United States, since it is so starkly in contrast to the "Wealthy Doctor" character. While our focus is on the examination of how doctors are making changes to their own practices, as a reaction to the medical system, to the detriment of patient care, I'd like to present a glimpse into why suggestions such as Medicare for All are incompatible with the practices of most physicians.

Firstly, take the example of the primary care practices I described earlier in this chapter, providing cosmetic service options for interested patients. One of these practices, with an excellent reputation, had to drop out of participating with Medicare several years ago due to the medical insurance reimbursement climate. It was a financial decision and fundamentally a sound one. The difference in the reimbursement from seeing patients insured by private companies compared to Medicare can be anywhere from 30–50%, or more. For a medical practice, this is the difference between being in the black versus the red. In the *Journal of the American Medical Association*, a physician wrote in response to a 2019 publication of the implications of "The Pricing of Care Under Medicare for All" that if the reimbursement to the physician for a typical office visit is $73, the overhead for many physicians during that time is close to $200.(72) Additionally, he notes that "My own family physician of 25 years had to drop me when I went on Medicare several years ago, as reimbursement was below his office overhead."

Now bear in mind the dynamic we have discussed. Physicians are on a treadmill of having to see more and more patients due to low insurance payments. This translates to less time per patient, as doctors attempt to stay afloat. Medicare's poor reimbursement is sharply compounded by the denials of common services, such as certain blood tests, medications, and radiology studies. In fact, Medicare has the highest rate of denials of any medical insurance system in the United States! In 2013, the American Medical Association (AMA) investigated denial rates by sampling 2.6 million electronic claims for 4.7 million medical services across 41 states. The AMA found that Medicare denied medical treatments and procedures more than three times the rate of any commercial insurance company.(73) This is an essential finding. If recommended treatments are being rejected at a three-fold greater rate than other insurances, and the reimbursement is distinctly lower, is it any wonder that doctors are *running* from Medicare?

Furthermore, Medicare has been found to be the slowest insurer at processing medical claims for services. They take two weeks on average to respond, compared to other insurances that average 7–10 days.(74) Where the rubber meets the road, in daily practice, that is a frustrating delay. Imagine you have a problem with your internet service and it takes an average of two weeks for someone to get back to you with an answer? And worse that this response may be quite dissatisfying.

Therefore, if suddenly there were not competing insurance companies in the US market, and if there was only Medicare, is it at all plausible that this processing time will improve? I sure don't think so. The government apparatus handling Medicare, known as the Centers for Medicare and Medicaid Services (CMS), is already clearly less efficient than commercial companies providing health insurance. Expanding Medicare also does not mitigate the reimbursement problem. Again, medical practices are currently dropping Medicare from their list of accepted health plans, and they are not at all excited to add more Medicare-insured patients to their panel. Doctors know that more Medicare patients means a larger fraction of relatively poorly reimbursed healthcare in the workday. Furthermore, they will confront even more denials for proposed medical tests and treatments in aggregate if more patients are insured through CMS.

Medicare expansion is likely unrealistic in today's political environment anyway, but the drawbacks of such a proposal are highly problematic. There is a good reason that "finding a policy approach that insures more individuals while attenuating projected increases in health care spending remains a goal that has been elusive for more than 5 decades of US policy making," as was published in the *Journal of the American Medical Association* in 2019.(76) But this is an important caution, as such proposals would even further strain the pressures doctors are facing, including the ones that are causing the exact maladaptations that we are discussing. This of course does not mean that we do not endeavor to formulate solutions, but there has got to be a superior path forward than to expand Medicare.

Case Progress Update:
The office Christmas party is wrapping up at a local trendy restaurant. As people are exiting late in the evening, the brightly burning torches offer tantalizing warmth in the crisp December air. Laughter continues to punctuate conversations. Dr. Phillips bids his staff adieu and strides to his car with a mixture of sleepiness and residual excitement. Turning on his BMW, he smiles quietly, thinking of his upcoming island getaway in the Pacific.

9

THE OLDER DOCTOR

Our next patient is a 70-year-old gentleman, Dr. Hippocra-
tes. But wait—his room is empty? Ahh, there he is; Dr.
Hippocrates is walking toward us. Undoubtedly, he's return-
ing from the break room on the ward, with a bag of chips
and coffee in his hands.

Dr. Hippocrates was one of those people who knew how to
make an entrance. With his long stride, sharp boots (he es-
chewed the hospital-issued slip-proof sandals on Day 1 of his
admission), and subtle nod toward us as he came to his
room, you quickly sense that he is "somebody." The nurses
love talking to him and always say they are "pulling for him."
He unquestionably has a certain quiet grandeur about him.
And it is not unwarranted: he trained with some of the most
famous cardiologists of the 20th century, including one who
is the author of the gold standard cardiology textbook. He
also published one of the seminal papers in cardiac arrhyth-
mias in the late 1960s, which has aged as well as he: it is still
relevant to clinical management to this day.

Alas, recent years have not been so kind. His large cardiology
practice, which he founded 35 years ago, now has all the
trappings of modernity, including fancy electronic medical
record systems. He still makes good money—but not great

money. And he wants to "slow down" but frequently frets about his income stream in retirement. Perhaps his constant pacing around the ward and recurrent coffee refills are a sign of this anxiety?

His younger colleagues often run cases by him since he has virtually seen it all and typically has clairvoyant medical advice. They forgive him for his repetitive (but fascinating) stories of training with the "giants of medicine" and how they "used to do it before all these fancy machines," all while "having only five real medications in the dispensary."

Trainees regularly rotate through the busy practice, and are sometimes caught quietly snickering as Dr. Hippocrates slams his mouse and mutters to himself. There is more audible laughter at that point, causing our good doctor to whip his head to the right. Turning to the students, he remarks, "It may be second nature for you, but I'm too old to learn to type. And definitely to learn computers!"

At that moment, one of the younger cardiology nurses briskly walks over to Dr. Hippocrates's workstation. The students overhear her mentioning "low BP" and "irregular." A patient in the clinic is having an immediate medical problem, possibly even a heart attack. Our gentlemanly physician does not look at the nurse directly, but purses his lips and nods understandingly. He tells her to obtain a "stat cardiogram." The nurse asks Dr. Hippocrates to "enter the order in the EMR" and she will then page the technician who performs EKGs. He then throws a penetrating glare at her as he says authoritatively after a deep breath, "You're telling me to put an EKG order in the computer first??! Jesus. Just run the damn EKG, the patient has an abnormal heartbeat! Orders can wait!"

***

T his very situation will disturbingly reverberate through clinics across the nation. Some administrators will support blindly adhering to the process of entering an order in the electronic health record before the next action can be taken, even if it may risk a delay in patient care. Alternatively, excuses such as "There's nothing we can do, this is the way the computer system is" will be thrown about recklessly. In this example of the EKG order, I have personally seen an eerily similar situation play out for a hospital patient. The doctors were in disbelief, as the EKG technician would not come unless someone ran to a computer to enter the order. The nurses who were involved even suggested that one alternative would be to call a "Code Blue", which is an alarm triggering assigned teams of physicians to employ life-saving measures for an emergent situation. However, this would have been an abject misuse of this alarm when the patient was clinically not in an unresponsive or similar state.

In these real scenarios, as well as others, virtually all doctors were displeased. However, in my observation, most older and more experienced physicians were especially appalled. Physicians who trained 35–40 years ago or longer were apprentices of a previous generation when the doctor welcomed the challenge and responsibility of taking superb care of the patient. It was an era when respect and income were even greater, and everyone recognized that, ultimately, this generation of doctors truly did typically know what was best for the patient's life and health. As such, I have great respect for this generation of clinicians: they had to meld expert knowledge, responsibility, and leadership in daily patient care. I am proud to have had some of them as my own professors. There was no Google to lean upon, nor did they need it. Thus, when a Harvard-educated cardiologist with 40 years of experience is told that an electrocardiogram will not be performed for a suspected arrhythmia or heart attack until the computer order is put in, he is rightly outraged.

This older contingent of physicians also despises "guidelines" for medical treatment. They see guidelines for what they truly are: at best, a general *guide* suggesting an approach, and not something that can be extrapolated to every patient with a given diagnosis. At worst, they are tools wielded to force certain medical decisions even if the doctor disagrees with the approach. The latter situation materializes as a result of health insurance companies rigidly adhering to a guideline to obligate the choice of a particular treatment; if this specific treatment is not chosen, then the insurance company will deny the coverage of the medication. The physician could potentially appeal the insurance company's decision, but this firstly may not be successful, and secondly the delay in awaiting a review of the appeal risks the patient's health. If I have to engage in the appeal process, I will inform the patient and warn them of the commensurate delay. I will also then discuss the pluses and minuses of alternative options so as not to risk the patient's health.

A calamitous consequence of the "cookie cutter" pitfalls of guidelines unfortunately befell one of my patients a couple years ago. A patient sought a consultation to assess her breast cancer risk, because her maternal aunt developed breast cancer in her forties. The most common gene that is tested is known as the *BRCA* gene, conferring a considerably elevated risk of breast and ovarian cancer. Due to these risks, some patients will choose to get a double mastectomy (both breasts surgically removed) to neutralize the breast cancer component of this gene. Many news articles have given a voice to those who have selected this option, thusly imbuing other patients with the strength to follow in their footsteps, for appropriate cases.(75) Guidelines have been published for when insurance companies will cover the patient's cost for getting the *BRCA* testing completed. However, the catch for my patient is that she is *adopted*. Her knowledge of her maternal aunt having had breast cancer was from the fruits of my patient's own investigation of her family tree; her biologic mother's or other relevant family members' health history was unavailable. In my medical view as an oncologist, the patient was rightly concerned about the potential for having an elevated inheritable breast cancer risk. Unfortunately though, she did not tick off enough boxes to "justify" her health insurance covering her *BRCA* gene testing.

Her only recourse at this point was to pay for the testing without any insurance coverage, but with a price tag of several hundred dollars, she felt she could not afford such an expense. We discussed options, and the patient chose to follow a more "standard" approach for breast cancer detection: mammograms coupled with breast examinations. As unsettling as this scenario is, an even more frightening aspect is the ovarian cancer development risk, if she indeed harbors the *BRCA* gene mutation. To date, there is not a reliably effective screening program for early detection of ovarian cancer. Therefore, if she has inherited this particular gene, she bears a real risk for ovarian cancer in the future.

Beyond rigid guidelines and illogically instituted processes, the older physician also abhors the use of the computer for so much medical care nowadays, spearheaded by the black hole of a time sink that is the EHR. I know multiple colleagues who are extremely bright physicians but are simply not "computer savvy." There is a strong generational component to this electronic acumen, akin to how I see my own children are proficient with computer technology at an even younger age than my own generation. I have actually witnessed a physician in the outpatient clinic thrash the mouse against the desk in frustration, just as our distinguished Dr. Hippocrates did. Recall the data about how physicians spend approximately 50% of the workday entering data in the computer: the slower the individual is with handling computers, then the more this time with the EHR will balloon. That simply compounds the aggravation for the doctor. Being slower at typing is also associated with this; typing speed is another variable accentuating time spent parked in front of the computer. I have physician friends who regularly come to the office for several hours on the weekend simply to complete charting! Cue the burnout shot clock.

Therefore, this type of doctor—the older, experienced physician—exhibits many behaviors that are a maladaptation to the system. The summation of dogmatic institutional processes, guidelines dictating how patients should be treated, and computers force excellent clinicians like Dr. Hippocrates to change. All too often, changing for the better is simply not realistic. Think of it this way: imagine asking a relative over the age of 75 or so to suddenly and proficiently learn Microsoft Excel or QuickBooks to do their home accounting. You can give all the guide books and tutoring course offerings you want, but the majority of this set of individuals will either think you have gone mad, get frustrated trying, or curtly give you feedback that it's so much easier with a pen and a proper notebook.

By and large, in the same manner, the older physician is asked to do the same. Frustration mounting and resistance to the forced changes are virtually inevitable. Pragmatically, the choices are few for Dr. Hippocrates and his generation: he either (a) retires, (b) bears the frustration to grind out the last few years to his planned retirement, or (c) leaves clinical medicine. Therefore in all these scenarios, either the physician exits medical practice or accelerates the timetable for retirement. Hence, this amounts to a brain drain of highly experienced doctors. As a result, the patient's long-standing relationship with their physician is severed.

Dr. Hippocrates cannot straightforwardly escape the dissatisfaction he is experiencing. Unlike the Idealistic Doctor, who is comparatively younger and can search for a new job, Dr. Hippocrates will find a shift to a new city or practice challenging. The reasons for this are numerous. For one, the EHR as the core repository of medical documentation is ubiquitous in the United States. It is exceedingly rare to find a clinic that still utilizes paper charts. Therefore, if Dr. Hippocrates accepted a new job at another cardiology practice, it is a virtual certainty that he will simply have to learn a new electronic system, replete with pitfalls comparable to what he is experiencing at his current practice.

Even the search for a new position is not so easy for the older physician. Analogous to corporate America, most practices and hospitals are looking to hire younger physicians. The reasons are multiple. For one, the typical clinic wants someone who may have a chance to practice for several years and not for just a brief stretch of two to three years prior to retirement.

Secondly, Dr. Hippocrates and his generation will command a higher income, particularly if one is a subspecialist like a cardiologist. The new residency graduate can be paid less by a significant sum; salary differences can exceed $200,000. Large institutions like hospitals would much rather pay a lesser salary—and not unusually consider hiring a physician assistant rather than a doctor (again, due to a drastic difference in salary, not a deficiency in training).

Thirdly, the experienced physician with over 30 years in medical practice will have deep roots in their local community. He or she is not eager to move to a new town or state. They know the community, have a close circle of friends, and own a home. This coupled with being fairly close to retirement anyway results in a high degree of job-seeking inertia. And the kicker is that very often doctors cannot simply accept another job in the same town due to the prevalence of noncompete clauses in most contracts. These clauses are incorporated to protect the employer, so a doctor cannot easily build up a large panel of patients, and then leave for a competing practice in the nearby vicinity. Since patients are generally loyal to their doctor; they often will follow them *en masse* if they do not have to travel much farther than where the doctor used to practice. Hence, transporting a few thousand patients to another practice can result in a loss of business for the original clinic.

So what recourse does the older physician have? There are a few options where one does not have to necessarily move from their hometown. For example, a colleague of mine facing a similar conundrum to Dr. Hippocrates but in the field of oncology took a job at a clinical research organization (CRO). He left his group practice entirely, unhappy with the changes taking place, but was not prepared to retire immediately. He parlayed his past medical research experience to join a CRO. For those unfamiliar, a CRO is an organization that deals with clinical trial logistics and execution. A pharmaceutical company will have initiated the trial for a drug in development, and then they will contract with a CRO to handle record-keeping, paperwork, monitoring, and site visits. For my colleague, he confesses that he does miss the conversations with patients, and the direct medical care of being a clinician. He notes having to travel much more frequently nowadays as well. In the same breath, however, he also shares that "his days of being on-call at a hospital are over" and that he does not "have to stay up late doing dictations." He is generally free on the weekend as well. As he is close to retirement, anyway, he is satisfied with the balance of receiving a steady paycheck with much less stress compared to active practice.

Another way to escape the burdensome grind of modern medical practice is becoming a case reviewer for health insurance companies. To some, this is something of a "if you can't beat 'em, join 'em" approach, but one that may be a good fit for some individuals. A colleague of mine was a family practice physician in New Jersey and then, fed up with the litany of tribulations of clinical practice, accepted a position at a medical insurance company, tasked with adjudicating requests for medical procedures by doctors and other clinicians. They may have to either reject (or approve) a requested study or medication based on the insurance company's rules or have to discuss a case with a clinician directly in the event of an appealed denial decision.

To many practicing physicians, this role working with health insurance companies may not be as humanistically fulfilling, being a desk job without any patient contact. On the other hand, this is one path by which one can escape toiling in modern practice and often can work from one's home. And like the option of clinical research, there is no on-call or weekend work. In the case of my colleague in New Jersey, he continued this work until his retirement.

Thus, we can see the predicament of the older doctor. Highly trained and with decades of experience, he has much to offer in terms of a patient's medical care. However, the onslaught of changes to the healthcare system as a whole drastically conflict with the older doctor's skillset. The very notion of being told by insurance companies to treat patients differently, rather than drawing from their vast database of experience, is unfathomable for many. Disillusioned by these global changes, and unable to smoothly transition to this new world, the older doctor is left with but a few viable options; furthermore, these options generally lead to a quicker exit from active medical practice. This is a loss for the healthcare of Americans everywhere.

10

THE ADRENALINE JUNKIE

Our next patient on the ward is—Whoa, what's going on here? Dr. Halstead is blitzing down the hallway toward a "scrub sink", where doctors and nurses properly wash their hands and arms prior to a surgical procedure, at breakneck speed. This guy is clearly athletic, and has the presence of a star wide receiver sprinting down the sideline. The medical personnel and others are effectively paralyzed watching him; everything is in slow motion compared to Dr. Halstead in this moment. Now look at this—Dr. Halstead just punched the scrub sink's metal facade three times, like a boxer!! "YEAH!! Let's see some patients!!!!" exclaimed Dr. Halstead, his baritone voice resonating through the entire ward. I must admit, I unquestionably can feel the energy too, like I want to help out with… a medical emergency? But wait a minute—Dr. Halstead is a patient here. He has amazing surgical dexterity in the operating room, but he's not treating anyone right now. What in the world is he doing?

Like a sonic boom in the wake of a fighter jet, a murmur grows amongst the nurses on the ward. "At least this outburst wasn't at 4:30 a.m. like on Tuesday," one is heard saying to a colleague. A review of his chart reveals that Dr. Halstead has grown increasingly frustrated with surgical practice. He loves—nay, lives for—the rush of the life-saving operation. He wants to be in the thick of the pressure to save a patient from the brink of death. That's why he chose surgery as his specialty, and has practiced general and trauma surgery for 20 years. However, he's seen his income go down with decreasing insurance reimbursement, and a couple years ago he and several other doctors on a case got sued for a complication that was unrelated to and occurred two weeks after an operation he performed. Never one to back down from a fight, Dr. Halstead went off in a shouting match with the hospital administration for lack of support, and the relationship was subsequently so badly damaged that he resigned and moved to a different state. But unexpectedly, in his new group practice there is a whole other set of hospital politics with his surgical brethren.

Dr. Halstead knew he wanted to be a surgeon the first day he set foot in an operating room in medical school. He embraced the pressure, and he has both the mind and surgical skills to perform world-class work. He wants to get paid what he firmly believes he is worth, with the right team around him to allow him to operate and save lives. But instead, he is embroiled in fighting with hospital administrators, fending off lawsuits, and facing a decreasing income. He feels like he is boxed into a corner, and the path ahead in medicine is hazy at best. Dr. Halstead has been heard wondering aloud, looking downward, "What's next? A career change? Is that even possible?" For someone with such an elite skill set and passion for his work, shifting gears away from surgical practice entirely is perhaps a thought even more paralyzing than when we watched him in awe as he sprinted to the scrub sink.

***

W hat is arguably the most common medical scene in a television drama? By far and away, my observation is that it is when a patient is on the brink of death, and then a medical team launches into life-saving measures to save the patient. There will be multiple defibrillator shocks, doctors emotionally giving their most exhaustive effort with chest compressions, all topped with dramatic music. These measures to save the patient are successful in these scenes overwhelmingly often.

The sobering truth about cardiopulmonary resuscitation (CPR)–based efforts is that they revive the patient only 20–25% of the time.(80) So why are such scenes a frequent centerpiece of dramas and also quite popular with audiences? As the reader can surely appreciate, the answer is that they are pulsating, emotional, and ooze with a primal violent streak. It's good theater. Furthermore, it's akin to how car chase scenes laden with breakneck speed, crashes, fires, and testosterone are so popular in movies, although we've all watched them countless times.

Among medical professionals, surgeons and ER physicians (the latter more properly called "emergency medicine" physicians) are two of the specialties that deal with such scenes in real-life practice. The "romantic" image of these adrenaline-pumping life and death moments are central to what draws these individuals to become a surgeon or ER doctor in the first place. Though, of course, this is not indicative of everyone's thought process, for most ER doctors I know, the life-threatening potential surgical case is much more exciting than the unkempt patient with alcoholism in the emergency department for the third time that week, or the well-dressed runner with good insurance who could have easily gone to her primary care physician the next morning for ankle pain rather than to the ER.

On the other hand, it is also quite reasonable that the patient on the brink of death should get more medical attention. If a patient may decline at any moment, the doctor needs to prioritize that case and comb through the details as quickly as possible. However, therein lies the problem. Those patients in the ER with less exciting conditions will not get the same attention from the doctor. In fact, I'll bet that you'll be lucky to see the doctor more than once, and even then, just for two minutes. If you expect something more, you'll be disappointed.

This is not to imply that these doctors do not care, but rather, certain cases simply have to be triaged as more critical ones. After all, there are only a limited number of medical personnel in the ER at any given time. Furthermore, the degree of excitement of a given case is typically intertwined with the acuity of the patient.

Another key driver of why you'll be lucky to see the doctor again is the pressure from the hospital of minimizing a patient's time spent in the emergency department. This bears emphasizing: in speaking with a number of my emergency medicine physician colleagues, hospitals exert significant pressure on the ER doctors. The reason for this is that the hospital has to consider the operational logistics, and from that perspective, the medical teams have to keep the patients moving, lest the ER amass a substantial backlog of patients. New patients are constantly coming into the facility. Data from a study incorporating over 200,000 patients over two years in relatively populous areas, showed that this equates to approximately 20 patients per shift.(77)

There has been a significant body of literature in the realm of emergency department efficiency. One analysis states that the top problem stemming from a long wait time in the

ER is patient dissatisfaction. Among the noteworthy consequences of this issue is that some patients will leave before even being examined, and others will never formally check in to the ER upon inquiring about the wait time. This particular analysis estimates that this could result in the loss of up to 10% of the potential volume of patients seen in a day!(78) Furthermore, this can cascade into poor patient reviews of the hospital. If you have any doubt this makes hospital administrators concerned, take a look at those large roadside billboards displaying a supposedly real-time "wait-time clock" of the local ER next to a picture of a smiling doctor or nurse with perfectly styled hair.

Therefore, for a given hospital, this translates into substantial revenue potential. Hence, there is high motivation to drive the patient down one of the two roads out of the ER: discharge the patient home or admit the patient to the inpatient unit. (Technically, there is a third road also.) Beds have to be available to accommodate new patients coming in. In other words, if more patients are able to be seen in aggregate, this increases both patient satisfaction and revenue.

Now this sounds generally reasonable so far, but here's what is disturbing about some of the strategies to attain the desired decrease in wait time. One strategy to speed things along is to order all tests you possibly will need from the beginning of the workup.(78) Therefore, the doctor often will not wait for the first few results to return to more intelligently guide further testing *only if necessary.* Rather, order all of it, along with the associated sum cost of all those blood tests and radiology scans. Then, one will have more data to quickly come to a diagnosis and treatment plan. Speed is the name of the game, no?

Ordering large panels of testing is even more inevitable due to one of the key methods to hammer down the wait-time clock. In a number of emergency departments, part of the protocol is that, upon a patient checking in, the doctor should introduce herself to the patient and then promptly initiate the medical workup. In other words, the doctor has not actually had a chance yet to formally evaluate the patient; rather, she knows the "chief complaint" of the patient, courtesy of the intake nurse, and then for a given symptom orders the pertinent panel of testing. Consequently, the patient's wait-time is reduced dramatically, to only minutes! Therefore, one technically can point out that the doctor had face-to-face time with the patient and that there are time-stamped medical orders. Ergo, the patient cannot say he has been waiting for longer than an hour, even if the physician comes again later to better interview the patient.

As an example of these empiric panels of testing, consider the following scenario. If someone is complaining of abdominal pain, an emergency medicine physician may have a general order set including the following:

- intravenous fluids with normal saline
- antinausea medication
- antacid-type medication
- blood work for a complete blood count, comprehensive metabolic panel, amylase, and lipase
- abdominal X-ray or ultrasound
- no food or drink

However, these may not all be necessary. These type of generic panels for a common symptom is often dubbed a "shotgun approach" among physicians. The philosophy being "Yes, we don't need all of these, but if we order everything, we'll probably figure out the diagnosis." Appropriate testing really hinges on the details of the patient's history. But if the doctor is under pressure to keep the wait time very low, there is virtually no escape from engaging in a slew of simultaneous investigations. Also, beyond revenue, the hospital has other pressures to implement such wait-time reduction methods also; these include longer wait times affecting the prestige of the facility and poor patient satisfaction leading to low survey scores. Recall the importance of Press Ganey and similar surveys and their link to reimbursement.(31)

On this basis, another proposal for improving emergency department efficiency is that the ER doctor doesn't "have to wait until all tests are back before setting a plan of action for treatment."(78) The implication is that one can anticipate the proper treatment based on the patient's symptoms and the doctor's clinical experience. However, if that is the case, why order the extra tests that one is not waiting to see, in the first place? Again, a huge driver of this is the link of reducing wait time, increasing efficiency, and producing greater revenues. If doctors use this approach for all patients, then efficiency will be maximized, and ultimately the bottom line fattened.

The kicker is that the extra testing will be billed to the patient and insurance companies as well! In other words, there is no disincentive to request a large panel of medical tests for standard complaints. Now, I feel that the hospital should get reimbursed for tests performed and medications administered, but some fraction of these can be avoided if doctors had a chance to work in a more logical progression.

As one ER staffing consulting group framed it, the emergency department medical service can be fast and "cheap", or fast and "good", but not "fast, cheap, and good".(79) A classic example illustrating this is the management of a sinus infection. If a patient presents to an emergency department with sinus complaints, he may have blood tests ordered, medications administered for symptom management (e.g., pain medications for a sinus headache), empirical antibiotics, and a CT scan of the sinuses. So what's the bill for all this? It will be a staggering sum, likely ranging between $2,000 to $4,000. In addition to the blood tests, radiology studies, and medications, there is a bill for the doctor's fees, the hospital "facility fee", and the radiologist's fees for interpreting the CT scan images. Contrast this with the patient having gone to his primary care physician: he would have paid the fee for the doctor office visit and possibly for an antibiotic, which would have totaled about $200. That's an approximate 10- to 20-fold difference in cost!

The next recommendation in this list to improve the ER doctor's time efficiency is to "delegate as much as possible."(78) This is a key tact in adhering to the mantra of speed. With many emergency departments only staffing one to three physicians per shift, the M.D. is a limited resource to go around. Therefore the more laborious the shift, the less time is available per patient for each physician. Undoubtedly, the experienced emergency department physician is skilled at deploying his personnel to appropriate tasks required in patient care. A nurse is administering a needed intravenous antibiotic for one patient, a respiratory therapist is providing inhaler treatment for the asthmatic in distress, a medical assistant is checking the blood pressure, and a physician assistant is reassessing a wound that has been sutured. Particularly in the more hectic emergency rooms, the physician cannot realistically do all this for 20 patients per shift either efficiently or effectively without assistance from the rest of the team. This dovetails into patient contact with the physician. With the concentration on maximizing patients seen in the ER, this is why time is simply not available to see a patient more than once or twice. Moreover, these encounters with the physician are fleeting; each time the doctor comes, it will likely be for less than five minutes and. often closer to one to two minutes.

In my research, I've spoken with multiple ER physicians who work in different states for their perspectives on these issues of modern emergency medicine. One of the most common threads I've heard is that of patient safety. I can't help but sense that ER docs are almost whispering this to me, because it is one of their deep concerns. Recall the classic axiom in medicine, primum non nocere: first, do no harm. Friends and colleagues who have shared this concern have told me that they are almost *hoping* that in the frenetic rush of triaging patients, keeping the wait-time clock low, charting, and billing, they are not inadvertently endangering a patient. I surmise that, most of the time, patient cases are able to be addressed in a safe manner, and the instances diverging from the normal professional standard of safety are occasional or perhaps rare. However, when someone's health or life is at stake, this is ultimately not acceptable. Ideally, doctors would have a case load they can realistically see safely and have sufficient time to complete an intelligent, thoughtful workup grounded in medical science. However, this is plainly not the reality in the United States currently.

This hit home for me when I had to take my son to the emergency department once for a cut suffered from a sports injury on the field. I was concerned there was a chance he may need stitches, and as it was already into the evening, I had to go to the ER because the pediatrician's office was closed. (Plus, the pediatrician would not typically suture a cut.) The hospital where I went was one where I have staff privileges. Generally, I try to downplay being a physician when I'm out around town with my family, but in this instance, I thought it would be useful to bring my hospital identification badge and mention casually to the intake nurse that I'm an oncologist. All of the staff were professional and courteous, but initially the ER doctor did not even come once to assess the injury! As a physician myself, a key reason I was taking my son to the ER was so the requisite specialist—a doctor trained and board-certified in emergency medicine—could provide his opinion about needing sutures or not. My clinical sense was that sutures were not needed, but I sought the assessment of the ER doctor. Furthermore, I also thought at least I would see the doctor once, after the nurses and physician assistant came. Eventually I had no choice but to insist on the doctor to come to the bedside; the doctor came reasonably promptly after I asked, and after a careful examination, he reassured me that sutures were not necessary.

This personal anecdote was quite edifying for me. Being in the medical field, I understand and have observed first-hand the dynamics of emergency department flow, maximizing patients seen, and the pressures on the doctor. However, I believe good medicine is inextricably connected with the physician stopping by the bedside for a physical complaint such as an injury. In the preceding experience, I had to resort to insisting he come to examine my son, along with feeling I needed to flash my hospital ID badge. I cannot help but wonder: if I could not speak up with the confidence of a physician, and have my badge, would I have received this attention? Would the average person coming into the emergency department with their child have seen the physician? My gut sense, unfortunately, is that the answer is more likely to be no.

I should clarify a fundamental point: this does not mean that the medical staff does not care. I strongly believe they do care and are trying their best. Every emergency medicine doctor I know and have discussed this with would love to spend time with each patient if it was realistic. But with the pressures of keeping patient cases humming in and out of the emergency department, she simply does not have time. This segues into another time-management recommendation for emergency departments, which is "don't waste free time."(78) On this point, we have not even touched on the deepest time sink beyond juggling 20 patients per shift and delegating to appropriate medical team members: charting. This is also arguably the most glaring thing missing in the television drama *ER*; virtually no one is seen entering notes into the chart. (After all, on television, a patient getting emergency surgery is exciting, not doctors spending a couple hours typing in a chart) Also bear in mind that in the era of ubiquitous electronic health record systems, even more time is spent charting than in the past (*ER* reflected the predominant usage of paper charts in the 1990s). Before the doctor goes home upon completion of her shift, the charting needs to be finalized, particularly for the hospital to be able to promptly bill the insurance company.

Therefore, "don't waste free time" translates into every free moment possible being applied to getting the paperwork done. This is not to mention the spate of other interruptions for the ER doctor, such as phone calls and questions. They are not working in a vacuum. There is also evidence that this cavalcade of clinical responsibilities triggers fatigue and inefficiency later within the doctor's shift, as well.(77) The human experience informs us that it is simply difficult to be as chirpy and eager to engage in dialogue with others, such as new patients, toward the latter parts of a busy work shift.

Now, completing the documentation in the patient charts is tied to billing the insurance companies for reimbursement. Naturally, all hospital departments want to submit insurance claims as soon as possible to sustain the flow of revenue. With the aggregate dollars at stake, doctors are under pressure to "close" charts as soon as possible; the complexity of the visit and other features of a case have to be recorded in a certain manner to provide evidence that the amount billed to the insurance company is reasonable. If patient notes were not promptly completed, the aggregate pending insurance charges could quickly spiral out of control. This signing off on cases also includes cosigning charts seen by a physician assistant or nurse practitioner. For billing purposes, the doctor signing off on charts seen by these aforementioned colleagues allows for a higher amount to be billed to the patient's insurance.

There's an old saying from medical school from a popular book that we studied in our surgical rotations, entitled *Surgical Recall*. The author wrote that the perfect surgical student has to have a steel bladder, cast-iron stomach, and a heart of gold.(81) That is, if one is to emulate the model student, you should minimize "extraneous" activities and distractions, such as urinating and eating, while giving it your all for the sake of the patient. Well, with the pressure exerted on emergency department physicians and staff to have patients seen with maximum speed, this saying is apropos to modern emergency medicine. One of my old friends from med school, who is an ER doctor, quipped that "On many shifts, we don't even have time to urinate until after we're done."

This strategy of speed begets patient satisfaction begets increased revenue bothers me as a physician. In medical school and training, we are taught to order the correct tests that correspond to the likelier possibilities explaining a patient's predicament. Ordering larger numbers of tests to speed things along just reeks of a "don't think, just do" approach that goes against my medical training.

Ditto for engaging in a treatment plan before test results are back. I can vividly imagine my internal medicine residency professors admonishing me for suggesting something like that. "If you know and can justify your course of action, then why did you order the extra test?", my professors might have very likely said. One of my program directors had another saying, too, which is a corollary to the preceding question: "If you order a test you don't need, you'll get a result you don't want." Ergo, what happens when the extra test doesn't flow with the recommended treatment?

Thus the question is, do the ends justify the means? Is the efficient discharging of patients and whittling down of wait times worth it, in terms of good medical practice? I agree that decreasing wait time is an admirable goal, but this ultimately misses the mark. Hospitals are not wrong for considering patient satisfaction and department revenues. These are clearly important variables in the viability of an emergency medicine service. After all, emergency departments have to fundamentally be profitable, and not in the red, as they are providing a critical service to the community. But here you can see the reality of rushing to tick boxes, not having time for docs to think, and minimal time with the patient. For me as a physician, the environment created by these variables does not pass the chief litmus test of "Is this how good medicine should be practiced?"

Between these myriad pressures and the requisite charting and computer order entry work, there is simply not
time for doctors to adequately solve the problems they
confront on a daily basis.

This state of affairs is what leads to ER physicians to maladapt to these pressures. Many have no choice but to focus
on the "exciting" cases as a priority, due to the time crunch.
This cornerstone of triaging philosophy dictates that the
sickest patients need to be tended to preferentially. In my
discussion with these colleagues, the attitude is "Well,
things are so crazy sometimes, at least we can try to save
those that need our help foremost."

Another maladaptation by ER doctors is the trend of leaving emergency departments altogether and, instead,
practicing in settings such as free-standing urgent care
centers (i.e., those that are not connected to a hospital).
This translates to a loss of top doctors from the places that
need them the most: busy hospitals and their emergency
departments. Doctors who make this move sometimes
even sacrifice pay, feeling that it is a worthwhile trade as
their job satisfaction skyrockets. They are able to spend
more time with patients and, thereby, have sufficient opportunity to deliberate on symptoms and solve cases. This
fundamental point of satisfaction is a critical one. Similar
to stories on the television drama *ER*, doctors can dig into
cases, including ones that get the adrenaline going, and still
have enough time to come to a more satisfactory solution.

Then there are those who leverage their medical degree,
experience, and expertise to seek out entirely nontraditional routes. One such example is an emergency medicine
colleague I encountered who owns a laboratory company
focused on specialized testing. Specifically, this testing is

used by a completely different medical specialty, allowing for the rapid diagnosis of specific pulmonary illnesses. Furthermore, he has been quite successful in this arena, as he has smartly solved a pressing problem for an important test in outpatient subspecialist offices. From the perspective of job satisfaction, this colleague feels he has made a unique, valuable contribution to medicine, albeit by very nontraditional means.

Now, recall a fundamental detail in these maladaptations: it is occurring from the perspective of good medical practice and the health of the general public. In other words, the ER physician leaving the frenzy of an overloaded hospital ER and moving to an urgent care facility is perhaps a wise career move for the individual doctor. Again, this allows her to focus on cases, follow up details, perhaps decrease work-related stress, and attain improved job satisfaction. However, by her exiting the busy hospital emergency department, that is a loss for the greater local community that needs these emergency services. They lost a talented physician due to the multiple problems in modern emergency departments, such as the emphasis on churning through high numbers of patients, shotgun test ordering, and the incessant burden of charting.

The other take-home point for the reader is about helping to understand expectations. Having a more comprehensive knowledge of the problems in the system will allow one to see the key drivers of why the slew of tests and X-rays were ordered, and why one may be fortunate to see the ER physician once for just a few minutes. My anecdote when I took my son to the ER has adjusted my own expectations as well. Even as a physician, I anticipated a detailed examination and high-quality discussion with my emergency medicine colleague, but this did not materialize. The medical system is causing incalculable strain on highly skilled doctors, and this restrains them from applying their training such that they can practice medicine the way they would ideally prefer.

In addition to emergency medicine doctors, the other main group of "adrenaline junkies" in medicine are surgeons. These specialists live for the blood-pumping pressure of operating on a patient to try to save their life or halt a terrible illness in its tracks. Think of the patient who has a failing heart valve, and the top-notch cardiac surgeon sutures a new mechanical valve in its place, radically and immediately improving the patient's cardiac status. There is a profound miraculous quality to even being able to pull off something like this. Just a few decades ago, the same patient would have invariably declined and ultimately succumbed to heart failure. But now, the patient can truly have a new lease on life.

Such hyperskilled surgeons should be encouraged, and their profession nurtured, as they are truly making a difference in people's lives. But we saw what obstacles our paragon of a surgeon, Dr. Halstead, was facing, including a declining income and concern about lawsuits. These are but two of the core factors that have altered the landscape of surgical practice in the United States.

The revolutionary changes with health insurance companies determining reimbursement for professional services is the first crucial variable. As we discussed in an earlier chapter, doctors generally have little choice but to contract with large insurance carriers. As a refresher, this is because almost all patients will have some form of health insurance, and as they are already paying for this, they will typically seek out a physician who is within their network. Related to this, as most other physicians will be contracted with insurance carriers, the doctors not accepting a certain health plan will lose out on a sizable fraction of potential patients.

The downstream consequences of doctors being corralled into health insurance contracts is that reimbursements have declined. Therefore, the surgeon's income has decreased substantially over the years. For many surgical procedures, this diminution in reimbursement is particularly pronounced. An eye-opening one is a knee replacement, known as a total knee arthroplasty. In an analysis from 1992 to 2007, the absolute change in reimbursement from Medicare had decreased 19% over those 15 years. To adjust for inflation and the change in the cost of goods, this investigation used the consumer price index to adjust for these variables; after this adjustment, the decrease in reimbursement in real dollars is a staggering 44%.(81) Even a common operation such as an artificial knee confers risk, such as serious bleeding, infection, and possible blood clots. Furthermore, years of training are required to perfect this operation. In surgical fields, the aphorism of "Practice makes perfect" rings very true. Those surgeons who are more experienced with a given procedure generally have a lower complication rate, often an impressive 90% or greater improvement compared to less experienced surgeons.(82) Overall, the annual rate of decrease in reimbursement broadly in general surgery is about 3.5% per year.(83) Bear in mind that, with cost of living and inflation, goods and services generally become more expensive, not less.

Therefore, with striking and consistent decreases in reimbursement for common surgeries, such as the 44% decrease in knee replacement payment rates, surgeons' incomes have decreased substantially over the years. One reflection of this is the percentage of surgeons who have moved to employed positions rather than owning their medical practice. An analysis from 1983 to 1986 revealed that, in the 1980s, a mere 13.0% of general surgeons and 14.5% of surgical subspecialists were employed. In addition, approximately 50% were solo practitioners.(84) Contrast that to more than 30 years later, when up to 75% of surgeons were toiling in *employed* positions! Even a more recent time point for comparison informs us that in 2005, a paltry 19% of searches were for an employed surgical position (without an opportunity to become a managing partner in the business).(85) Notably, there is a gender difference in this trend, where one analysis found that 66% of male surgeons were employed, whereas 75.5% of female surgeons were employees and not owning the business.(86)

For me, seeing this trend in surgeons giving up owning their own businesses to this incredible degree, triggered a long, low whistle of surprise. General surgeons have indeed felt the pinch. After years of elite training, managing surgeries laden with risks, and the commensurate pressure, having the income decline to the point that the vast majority are giving up their businesses is a shame. Sure, running your own business successfully in any field necessitates a seemingly Herculean combination of attention to detail and broad effort. But the potential profitability has to be worth the effort one is investing. For example, let's say one takes on all the risks financially and professionally for a business and pours in 12 hours a day or more. Imagine if at the end of the year, your net profit is only twenty dollars. Obviously, that sounds ludicrous, and the point is that there is a threshold, below which one will simply not be willing to manage the enterprise. Now, what this threshold is for a typical general surgeon is somewhat intuitive (i.e., it depends on the individual and their circumstances) and can vary across a spectrum. Nevertheless, the bottom line is that the risks have increased (financially and medicolegally), while income has decreased such that the final math has many surgeons jumping ship for employed positions.

This also has serious consequences in terms of professional motivation. Twenty years ago, when I was in medical school, surgeons would proudly say they were able to not only take on the technical demands of an operation but also smoothly handle the perioperative medical management. Your surgeon would be personally involved with you, the patient, the entire way. Now, that point of pride has faded dramatically. The prevailing attitude is "It's not worth the risk" and "I'm not being reimbursed enough." Therefore what's happening in hospitals around the country? The surgeons are transferring patients to internal medicine or hospitalist colleagues, often only a day or two after the surgery is completed. This readily happens when the patient has other medical complexities such as hypertension or diabetes that are preventing a safe discharge home. Not too many years ago, however, the surgeon would still have spearheaded such situations. He would be there with the patient for the whole duration, ensuring quality of patient care and inspiring both confidence and comfort for the patient. Sure, he may consult a cardiologist or some other colleague for advice, to do what is best for the patient, but he would not be itching to transfer the patient to another doctor. In fact, nowadays, surgeons requesting a "transfer to medicine" (meaning, internal medicine colleagues) can often instigate professional arguments in many wards across the nation, with internal medicine colleagues pushing back that there are still active postoperative issues that are outside the scope of their training.

The surgeons who still admit their own patients and keep them under their care throughout a hospitalization are few and far between in modern times. One of my long-time urology colleagues commented that his group is one of the few surgical specialties that still take care of their own patients in this manner in my local area. It should not greatly surprise the reader that he is also a managing partner in his own practice. The attention to patients, extra level of service, and concern about one's reputation is clearly more acute when it is one's own business. I find this trend peculiarly ironic, as surgeons have to extensively wash their hands and arms immediately prior to a surgery and now are often figuratively washing their hands of a patient's case shortly after the operation is done.

To illustrate this preceding point, I had a case a few years ago, when a patient of mine with chronic leukemia was admitted to the hospital for persistent fevers. When I was rounding on my patients on a Friday afternoon, I found on examination that the patient had an abscess in the groin area (a walled-off infection that requires surgical intervention in addition to antibiotic therapy). Now, even in medicine, no one is eager to be given extra work late on a Friday. Being mindful of this, and prefacing my request with an apology, I called up a local private surgeon. Not only did he call me back promptly and was extremely courteous, but he saw my patient within an hour of discussing the case, and then had the patient scheduled for the operating room for first thing Saturday morning! Now that is called proper service, and it equates to very good medical care. In my personal experience, when it's your own business or reputation on the line, I have observed this distinct trend that these physicians are the ones who are the most willing to assist on a case—late Friday evening or not.

The other major pressure for both of our adrenaline junkies—surgeons and emergency medicine physicians—is malpractice risk. A hefty fraction of surgical cases bear enormous risk. If one is not highly trained and quite careful, even so-called "routine" operations can go south. For instance, consider a cholecystectomy—the surgical removal of the gallbladder from the abdomen. The rate of uncontrollable bleeding is up to 1.9%, often emanating from the liver bed.(87) Infections can complicate about 3 out of 1,000 cases, and inadvertent injury to the intestines in about 0.35% of patients. Overall, studies have reported serious complications occurring in about 2.6% of cholecystectomies.(88) These types of risks—infections and bleeding—are par for the course of many surgeries.

As one can see, even common operations can be fraught with potential complications. Part and parcel with these issues is that the surgeon will be worried about the potential of a future lawsuit. Such concerns can accentuate the existing daily stress of a surgeon. Like our super-surgeon Dr. Halstead, surgeons relish being in the operating room and turning around the course of a patient's illness via the proverbial knife. They know there is stress involved and have been exposed to this since their earliest training. But throw on the additional concerns of a possible lawsuit, and the cumulative burden is not so simple to absorb. Both one's personal and professional life can quickly become strained. Colleagues may catch wind of such proceedings and may or may not be supportive. This can lead to battles with bosses, such as when Dr. Halstead felt he was being thrown under the bus by his administrators. We discussed earlier how respect, or the loss thereof, is a vital issue for almost all physicians. The rumors of a malpractice suit can snowball into erosion of this respect from your colleagues; this can be difficult to accept for a doctor. In effect, the sum of these possible complications can become the straw that broke the camel's back.

Furthermore, certain fields of medicine are more prone to the likelihood of a malpractice claim, with surgical fields leading this dubious category. In a review of claims over 25 years from 1991 to 2005, 15.3% of general surgeons annually faced a malpractice claim.(89) Contrast that to psychiatry, where the frequency of claims was only 2.6%. Neurosurgery and cardiac surgery had an annual rate of malpractice claims of nearly 20% each. Put in terms of the risk of a malpractice claim over one's career, this was calculated to be 80% in surgical fields by the age of 45. These numbers are quite sobering. When the risk if about one in six per year for a general surgeon in the United States, it is no wonder that these medical professionals carry the associated worry and stress.

In fact, there is data that the surgeon suffers substantial stress irrespective of the outcome of the alleged malpractice. In a survey of physicians who faced a malpractice claim, over 80% reported "significant emotional distress, no matter the claim's outcome."(90) The most frequent manifestations of distress were reported to be anger and negative mood. The emotional impact is deemed so taxing to the doctor, that a clinical entity termed "medical malpractice stress syndrome" has even emerged in the literature. The constellation of symptoms is posited as being a possible form of post-traumatic stress disorder.(91)

Physicians maintain malpractice insurance policies to protect themselves financially from potential claims. But it is far from readily affordable, and for higher risk fields like surgery, the costs are enormous. Data from the American Medical Association in 2017 revealed that the annual aggregate cost of premiums for an average policy for a general surgeon will set you back $42,000 per year if you live in Orange County, California, in the vicinity of Los

Angeles. If the surgeon practices in Nassau County, New York (near Manhattan), the annual cost is an eye-watering $135,000!(92) These costs are scarcely fathomable. Just to reiterate, these are the costs for just paying your insurance premiums for *one year* for *one surgeon*.

Therefore there is astonishing cost to carving out a malpractice insurance policy. For perspective, the annual cost of malpractice premiums for an internist in the Los Angeles area is about $8,300, and in Nassau County, NY it is $34,000.(92) Though significant, these are three- to four-fold less than the costs for a surgeon's policy. Thus, between the specter of potential malpractice claims made in surgical disciplines and the cost to guard against this possibility, is it any wonder surgeons are trying to wash their hands of certain cases once they feel their responsibilities are completed? The more a surgeon stays involved on a case, the more likely the odds are of something negative occurring, which could increase the risk to the surgeon. This is also why surgeons will often decline to operate on cases that are felt to be too risky both medically and from a legal point of view.

This cacophony of problems blanketing the surgical profession—decreasing income, declining motivation with shifting into employed positions, staggering malpractice risks and costs, and the associated medical malpractice stress syndrome—have forced surgeons to adapt, or rather maladapt, to their circumstances. The behaviors we have discussed are some of these already. For instance, transferring patients out of the surgeon's direct care and to a hospitalist colleague is one maladaptation. After all, the surgeon has a longer relationship with the patient and multiple discussions prior to the operation, whereas the hospitalist has in all likelihood never seen the patient before in their career. The hospitalist is also a well-trained and capable physician, but I can tell you that it is very different when I get a phone call from one of my own patients, in contrast to meeting a patient I've never seen before. With a new patient, I don't yet have detailed knowledge of the nuances of the case. There is an inherent discomfort associated with that, whereas with my long-term patient, I feel confident I am weighing the relevant variables of the case in answering a question. Therefore, in my view, it would equate to better medical care for the surgeon to be the captain of the ship and then consult other medical specialists as the need arises for a case. But with 15% of general surgeons facing malpractice allegations annually, the prevailing wisdom is that it is not worth the risk professionally or financially.

There was a time when a surgeon would almost never do this. Our fictional Dr. Halstead would have surely been chided by his professors, for the de facto admission that he cannot handle the medical complexities of a patient's situation. Alas, that assiduous style of practice is a rare breed nowadays, driven out of medicine by these headwinds.

Surgeons fleeing in droves to employed positions is another maladaptation. If they weren't facing the marked diminution in reimbursement for routine surgeries, declining anywhere from 20–45% (such as total knee replacements), and additionally enormous malpractice insurance premium costs, surgeons very possibly would not be running at all to employed positions. Recall that, prior to these sweeping economic shifts, over 85% of surgeons were in private practices.

As cited previously, a highly troubling consequence of this maladaptation is the diminishing motivation. Obviously there are exceptions, as I still see some surgeons who will be rounding at the hospital late into the evening on a routine basis, but at one time, this was the norm. As any business owner knows, there is a vast difference in perseverance and attention to detail when your own reputation and business is on the line. Medical professionals are definitely not immune to this dynamic. As altruistic and kind as some of us endeavor to be, it is woven into the fabric of human nature that no one will care for your own baby like you will.

Intriguingly, some surgeons have attempted to escape the pitfalls of the American surgical environment altogether. There are a number of doctors in various surgical subspecialties that will travel abroad to offer their expertise and training for specific procedures. For instance, some urologists travel to Mexico and a number of Caribbean islands to offer certain procedures that may not be normally available in those nations. Invariably, these are cash-paying patients, and hence, this neutralizes insurance reimbursement concerns altogether. Conversely, the doctor feels like his or her services are clearly being valued. This avenue of opportunity strikes a solid balance of fair pay for the technical expertise and risk of the operation, professional satisfaction, and patients receiving exactly the type of medical attention they are seeking.

This also touches on the broader trend of medical tourism. In the modern world of relatively affordable air travel (compared to the costs of even a few decades ago), there are many people around the globe who journey to obtain certain healthcare services. Fundamentally, this is borne of economic opportunity; people have a need for certain services, and of these, some feel they cannot get the requisite quality locally, and in turn, there are those professionals who are willing to come meet this need. Lastly, these prospective patients are willing to pay the asking price for this extra level of service. In Central America, as with the urologist example earlier, those who are able to pay for operations performed by surgeons trained in the United States will commute to locations in Mexico or the Caribbean. As these individuals are typically paying cash (and not via a medical insurance policy), they are making a conscious, thoughtful decision and carefully factoring in cost prior to undergoing a procedure. This is true to the way a market economy should function: goods and services are provided at prices determined by consumer demand and competition among choices.

A few other examples of medical tourism include patients from Saudi Arabia visiting India for specific procedures, such as knee replacement operations. In fact, one of the largest global centers for knee replacement surgeries is India, with the total cost of the operation a "mere" $1,000–1,500 (at current exchange rates at the time of this writing). Some centers will even offer white-glove service, in a sense, where the patient gets picked up from the airport, taken to a hotel, and later shuttled to the hospital. Contrast that with the United States, where the typical total cost will be a few thousand dollars! (93, 94) Remember you have to sum the copays for the preoperative visit with the surgeon, blood work, the bill for the surgery and anesthesia, and the postoperative care, including physical therapy. Therefore, depending on the costs for a patient in their home country, one can see why someone may travel for the operation, as it is worth it financially. Additionally, in surgical disciplines, higher volume correlates with better expertise and lower complication rates. Such global centers perform an extremely high volume of operations. This should also provide the patient with an added layer of comfort and confidence.

This can even be seen in reverse, in a sense, when a patient may come to the United States for a treatment because it is not available in their native country. I have had a few patients from Europe, who had the means to come to the United States expressly to participate in a clinical trial. In these instances, they were able to receive a cutting-edge therapy that otherwise they would not have had access to obtain. Particularly in those nations where there is a limited basket of cancer medicines available (which are generally expensive), there will be those treatments that simply will be unavailable, regardless of the patient's wealth. In my experience, these individuals were immensely thankful, both for coordinating their enrollment into the study (a logistically arduous process but made possible with the help of an excellent team) and because of the gravity of a diagnosis like cancer.

Though I am in a different field of medicine, being an oncologist, one thread is the same through all the tribulations of modern surgical and emergency medicine practice. One wants their physician to be able to think clearly and critically. With the palpable pressures of declining income, six-figure annual malpractice insurance premium costs, and a high risk of malpractice suits, the surgeon is shouldering multiple burdens when he or she sees you for a consultation. You don't want your doctor to be stressed out, for the sake of your own health, trust me.

Similarly ER doctors would love to explore every patient's case in depth but sadly cannot due to the pressures of minimizing wait times, strain of barely getting a single breather in a hectic 12-hour shift, and incessant electronic charting. Hence, superbly trained surgeons and brilliant ER physicians buckle under the coalesced forces of the current healthcare system and consequently maladapt. They are fleeing from the responsibilities and opportunities of owning one's medical practice and signing up for employed positions. Those who remain in private practice have discontinued performing certain operations due to the insurance reimbursement being unacceptability low. Others are jettisoning patients to other colleagues to minimize exposure to malpractice risk. Emergency medicine physicians who once lived for the blood-pumping thrill of saving the patient from the brink of death are bolting to more comfortable (and often professionally satisfying) urgent care centers; consequently, this is a loss for inundated hospital emergency departments.

And yet there are still those moments where I observe the surgeon removing his operating cap after the life-saving heart procedure and the ER physician making a rapid, astute diagnosis for a critical patient. I can't help but feel that these moments are fleeting, like grasping threads of a bygone era. Without a significant course correction, we will continue to see this exodus of these invaluable physicians from the traditional heart of their respective medical specialties.

11

THE PROFESSOR

Dr. McMuffin strolled down the hallway to his university office, quietly whistling along the way. On a whim, he turned into a break room on the right and poured some coffee. Every morning, someone turns on the coffee maker and has hot coffee brewing, but he has never seen who. The coffee was reasonably potable after he poured in a lot of cream and drizzled in sugar. He then arrived at his office and pressed the power button on his desktop computer. Suddenly, the login screen illuminated out of sleep mode; he must never have turned off his computer yesterday. He clicked the email program and there were 18 unread messages. Two were from his department chairman; he figured he'd quickly read those first and then sip his coffee as he sifted through the rest.

To: "Professor McMuffin" <profmuffin@verylargetower.edu>
From: "Chairman's Office" <medchairman@verylargetower.edu>
Subject: Clinic Schedule Change

Hello Cornelius,

Thanks for all you do for Very Large Ivory Tower University. We are making a few clinic schedule changes. Several other faculty members are having the same adjustment.

Now, in addition to Monday and Thursday mornings, your clinic hours will be extended into the afternoon on those days, and also we'll start a new Friday morning clinic for new consultations. The operations committee wants us to get in new patients faster.

The good news: Tuesdays and Wednesdays are unchanged. Also there was talk of a fourth clinic day, but good news there too, we held off on that one.

Thanks a Million,

Jack

Professor McMuffin reflexively held his breath and felt his jaw tense up. Thoughts raced through his brain: "How am I supposed to meet with my research nurse on Friday mornings now? And when do I work on my grant funding applications? I just can't attend those Monday lunchtime resident lecture sessions now; there's too much going on. I don't even want to think of all the extra notes and EMR messages with more patients!" Then he opened the next message from the chairman, momentarily half-closing his eyes to steady his irritation.

To: "Professor McMuffin" <profmuffin@verylargetower.edu>
From: "Chairman's Office" <medchairman@verylargetower.edu>
Subject: ICNM deadline

Hello Cornelius,

I'm reminding all the faculty about the upcoming deadline for research abstracts being submitted to the International Congress for Newsworthy Medicine. It's next Monday. We really need to have a big presence there this year, otherwise we'll always be behind Even Larger Ivory Tower University. I'm asking for 15 abstracts collectively from the faculty and am confident we can meet this goal. Just got to burn the midnight oil a bit.

How's that NIH grant application coming along btw? Let me know if I can help -

Thanks a Million,

Jack

At this point, Professor McMuffin was actually shaking his head in his office, staring at the second email without blinking. More clinic and more research? In the wake of more than doubling his clinic time, something's got to give, but what? And now the conference abstract deadline is less than a week away. He viscerally felt the time crunch like a suffocating pressure.

His coffee was getting cold by now, and he had barely had any after these two messages. Maybe he should come in on the weekend? The Professor just wasn't sure. Instead, he got up quite robotically from his chair and figured it was best to get to the clinic sooner and review his patient charts. It was going to be a long day. Burn the midnight oil indeed.

***

T he tradition of academic medicine is that of a select and relatively small group of physicians dedicated to research and teaching. They would be consulted on the toughest cases and spend the majority of their time on clinical science or laboratory research endeavors. Only a few universities would have more than a handful of doctors on staff in a given department. While doctors were expected to be generally productive, they were not expected to churn out large numbers of patients or generate substantial revenues. These physicians were also paid accordingly due to this dynamic; their university salaries were far lower than their colleagues in private practice. And most accepted this distinction, given the above tenets of the academic environment.

In current times, however, the landscape has sharply shifted. We reviewed earlier how many hospitals and universities are now highly profitable institutions. They are assertively competing for a larger portion of the dollars to be extracted from the health insurance pie. Also as stated before, endeavoring to obtain more of a cut of the pie is understandable—after all, like any business, their goal is to be profitable and ideally thrive in the local marketplace. It is the structure of the modern US healthcare system as a whole that has created this scenario. But to accomplish this pecuniary objective, hospitals have to engage in more procedures and treat burgeoning numbers of patients. After all, only by billing the medical insurance company can one receive the commensurate profit.

Recall the broad trend across the United States that hospital systems are briskly expanding by employing more doctors, buying independent medical practices, and billing at distinctly higher rates. Prices are marked up anywhere from double to many multiples higher.(7) With collective profits of over $1 trillion available in the healthcare industry, the game has clearly become one that revolves around money.

Therefore, with big bucks at stake, it should come as no surprise that today's physicians, whether in outpatient practices or large hospital systems, are under pressure to bill insurance companies. The pursuit of science, with institutional profit as a secondary concern, has irrevocably become antiquated. The hospital system becomes wealthy by seeing patients, performing procedures and laboratory tests, and running scores of X-rays and CT scans daily.

One of the few paths available for the "nonproductive" physician—that is, one who is not billing the requisite amount for his field to justify his salary—is to have independent research funding. Mechanisms for this include grants from the government and private institutions. But if one does not have sufficient grant funding coming in, then one had better look out and polish the resume; for this latter circumstance, university hospitals will quickly fire such physicians—and have done so.(95)

Price transparency is one approach to counter the price inflation that is propelling this profit motive. As reviewed earlier, hospitals and associated professional services therein account for 30–50% of healthcare spending in the United States.(2) Furthermore, the increase in costs incurred by hospitals is growing by about 5% year-over-year. In contrast, medication prices, while also clearly an issue, total less than 15% of overall spending, and the average rate of cost increase annually is 1%. (2, 96) Gradually, analysts and the public are waking up to how there is a cavernous spectrum of possible prices for a given medical service, such as a CT scan. Since 2019, the United States federal government has been pushing for price transparency for services provided so the consumer can be armed with the proper financial information to choose before obtaining a given procedure or treatment. Therefore not surprisingly, certain corners of the industry have put up resistance to this price transparency initiative. They understandably want to make a tidy profit, but they don't want the public to be aware of the specific prices they have negotiated with insurers.(2) But it is a promising start, and patients will be able to comparison shop via actual prices, rather than the black box model with private contracts that is the norm in the United States today. If supported by a framework of enforceable laws, price transparency has the potential to catalyze competition in local markets across the country.

In the academic hospital, the sad consequence of these considerable currents is that science has taken a back seat. Sure, medical research is alive and well in one sense, but many physicians with an aptitude for research are shunted into clinical positions. From a hospital administration perspective, more physicians need to be involved with direct patient care, so the target numbers for profitability can be successfully met. Therefore, proportionally fewer doctors are in the research arena, and those who remain primarily committed to research will generally possess grant funding, so the university does not need to directly pay them.

What is fascinating is that the historical idealism of academic medicine has collided with the big business that healthcare has become. As a result, the academic physician has received mixed messages, resulting in something of a partial disconnect regarding medical costs to the patient as well as cost to the healthcare system more universally. Sure, the academician is also surely aware that, nowadays, costs are rising, insurance plans frequently have high deductibles, and a host of therapies come at a premium. However, in my discussions with numerous colleagues, some of the critical nuances of these costs—particularly those aspects at the forefront of the systemic problems we are discussing—are lost behind the veneer of the university.

This aforementioned disconnect encompasses a few key variables. Firstly, and quite intriguingly, many academicians often have at best a superficial appreciation of the stark difference in cost between providers of a given medical service, such as among radiology centers that administer CT scans. However, I have encountered this question from patients countless times; it is often a variation of "I need a CT scan three to four times per year, so where is it more affordable?" As patients have queried me about this multiple times, I have directly inquired about the cost of a given scan among the local radiology offices and hospitals. The variation in price exceeds $1,000 to $1,500 *per CT scan* in my experience comparing prices among local options. With health insurance plans increasingly having high deductibles to pay prior to the plan kicking in, patients are definitely sensitive to the cost question. While this disconnect does not apply to every single doctor, of course, in my experience having worked in both academic and private practice environments, I have observed this to be true all too often. This was also the experience of several colleagues throughout the US to whom I've posed this scenario. This is not a personal criticism at all but, rather, the result of an idealistic mindset cultivated by the echoes of an academia that no longer applies to the modern world. I have seen intelligent doctors openly remark in meetings and conferences, "Luckily I don't have to worry about cost and reimbursement when I see patients." Now the latter may be somewhat true—the employed doctor on one level does not have to typically be concerned with the reimbursement the hospital receives—but *cost to the patient* is decidedly critical nowadays. As a physician, I feel that if we are not bearing this key variable in mind when debating our management approach for a patient's case, then we are not holistically comprehending modern day American healthcare. And in the absence of a solid holistic understanding, how can we as doctors expect to contribute to the solution to medical costs?

The method by how studies, such as how laboratory and radiology tests have to be ordered in many institutions is another fundamental barrier for academic physicians to develop a tactile sense of patient costs. In multiple large hospital systems, tests that are ordered in the EHR have a default choice for the location of the requested service. Almost invariably, the medical test requested will, by default, be performed at that specific hospital. This may be reasonable, but it definitely does not account for a potentially higher price tag nor does it give the patient the opportunity to comparison shop for the scan. If by chance the doctor wants the test conducted elsewhere, one generally has to go through additional steps within the EHR to select an "outside location." Once this is done, however, further steps still have to occur. Unlike the in-house test location, this order will usually not flow electronically to the appropriate scheduling personnel. Rather, the order will print out, and then it has to be physically hand-delivered to someone who can call the desired location to schedule the test. The reader can envision the ambiguity and chance for error even by this point in the process. The doctor's understandably emotional reaction at this point is along the lines of "This isn't worth the trouble, I'll just take the easier route to order a test with the default location." With the combination of frustration and perhaps wishing he were able to spend more time with research work instead of patients, he isn't even thinking about the cost part of the equation.

Other times, the institution may attempt to directly convince the doctor to order the in-house test rather than having it done elsewhere. A long-time oncologist colleague of mine, who is elsewhere in the US from where I practice, told me how once he requested a pathology specimen to be analyzed by a commercial laboratory for specialized testing. The cutting edge of oncology treatment involves discovering genetic mutations or cell-signaling alterations (like on-off switches inside cells) that are causing a cancer to survive and grow. There are several excellent commercial laboratories that carry out robust testing of a few dozen mutations and in a rapid fashion. After my colleague requested this analysis, he received a call from a pathologist at the institution where he worked; the pathologist spent over 15 minutes attempting to convince the oncologist to allow the hospital to run a new in-house test rather than the one at the private lab. My colleague related how, ultimately, he had to insist on running the test at the outside laboratory, emphatically conveying his concerns about the dramatically slower turnaround time for a result (two weeks versus four weeks), far fewer cancer genetic abnormalities tested, and his concern that his patient's case needed a test he had experience with. Finally, he was able to end this phone call that wasted valuable time in his clinic day. Now, bringing awareness of an available lab study is reasonable, but the approach here is questionable: to debate changing the laboratory for a test that has already been ordered, in the midst of the patient schedule, and then essentially arguing about it with the treating physician.

At one conference, I even witnessed an argument between two doctors—one from an academic institution and the other in a private practice—about how the large hospital can inquire into obtaining a discount on a medication or get them on a payment plan. The crux of the private physician's argument was that in order to get the patient on some form of a grant, the hospital has to be making significant profit in the first place. And this profit is driven by the higher prices for the same services that are cheaper elsewhere. The academic physician argued that, at least this way, the patient can afford a medication that they may not be able to afford otherwise.

While the academic doctor's point has merit as well, as some treatment is better than no treatment after all, from a higher bird's eye view, the overall healthcare system's prices are still being driven upward unsustainably by such a business approach. It reminds me of a dialogue exchange from the classic movie *Jurassic Park*. When the lawyer working with Richard Attenborough's character, Dr. Hammond, saw living dinosaurs roaming the park, he remarked, "We're going to make a fortune with this place." Dr. Hammond shot back, "This park was not built to cater only for the super-rich." At which point, the lawyer quipped, "Sure … well, we'll have a coupon day or something."

What's further ironic about this situation is there is a federal government program dubbed 340B, by which hospital systems can demonstrate that, if their patient population has a specific threshold fraction below a certain income level, the institution can purchase medicines at a profound discount. These deep discounts often fall in the range of 20% below normal acquisition prices. The hospital pharmacy can then bill insurances the normal contracted rate. So if a given pharmacy would have made a 5% margin at average purchase prices, this margin is boosted amply by the 340B drug purchase prices. Cue massive, flashing dollar signs.

While many feel the 340B program has good intentions, the real-world application of this has created an enormous profit motive.(97) Consider that this margin is per drug prescribed, so the more medicines that are dispensed via the hospital pharmacy, the steeper the absolute value of the profit. With large systems benefiting considerably, they are then able to build gleaming new buildings, buy out independent practices, and hire more physicians, prosperously growing the bottom line. From a business perspective, this is successful work by an institution's finance team to use this program in their operations. A market opportunity is being incorporated into the business plan. And there are some hospitals who truly need and benefit from discounted acquisition prices, due to their comparatively "poor" mix of insurance their patients have. But the net outcome of the system, as currently applied in practice, is not reflecting the mission of why the 340B program was created.

A central variable that has led to this aberration in motive is that there are no government stipulations as to where the profits garnered via the 340B program must be invested. When the Center for Regulatory Effectiveness, an independent think tank, analyzed the current landscape of how facilities utilize this drug pricing program, they generated a few main findings. Firstly, patients within 340B programs were prescribed both more medicines and also more expensive ones than those patients elsewhere. Secondly, for oncology treatment, 340B hospitals charged over twice as much in aggregate compared to non-340B practices. Thirdly, this think tank concluded that there is no solid data that the playing field is more level now than prior to the existence of the 340B program.(97)

Thus, this program has created a heightened profit motive to see more patients, and consequently prescribe more medications, by which the facility can then reap the benefits of the low 340B prices. In addition, as more independent practices are bought out and absorbed by hospital systems, effectively more prescriptions come under the umbrella of the large institutions. As a result, in academic centers, proportionally more clinician effort is spent on patients and, thereby, less on research endeavors. So a downstream effect of this is science takes a backseat. I know several academic physicians who used to see patients one to one-and-a-half days per week, with the balance of their time on research and teaching. Now, these same individuals are asked to see patients around three days per week. As there is only so much time in a day, something has to give—and that something is research.

In the same vein, some centers will allow research faculty to remain on staff only if the physician has garnered sufficient research funding.(95) If they cannot successfully acquire this, the doctor is told to do more clinical work. However, what has transpired in the several years is that research funding is comparatively harder to acquire than previously, particularly in the wake of the Great Recession of 2008. This has tilted the balance even more heavily toward clinical work. Universities used to be able to routinely support junior research faculty until they found their footing. That was the norm. Scientific research entails painstaking work, and in the tradition of science, there is no guarantee that a certain avenue of investigation will be fruitful. One may strive to answer a research question via experiments for months to years, and ultimately the study can be "negative," in that something new is not discovered. While there is scientific value to answering "no" to questions as much as "yes", so to speak, negative studies will not make it into the major scientific journals and will typically not be deemed worthy of prestigious research grants. The aim of such grants, after all, is to monetarily support further efforts in a fruitful line of research.

The reader can thus see why science suffers. Junior faculty are often given a timeline within which they must acquire sufficient research funding. If they do not, these intelligent, scientifically curious physicians typically get shunted into clinical work. This is also noble work, of course, but it is sad that their hopes and enthusiasm for an academic career were short-circuited for money reasons. Another common route for these researchers is to work for a pharmaceutical company and join their drug discovery teams.

Therefore, the modern academic physician cannot easily be the academic of yore nowadays. Even those who can effectively navigate these waters have to proportionally spend more time with clinical work. That their aptitude for scientific work could not be cultivated more fully is a loss for the medical field as a whole.

Yet another pivotal way the academic doctor has maladapted to problems of modern healthcare is in the realm of education. A vital function of the academician is to educate the next generation of physicians. But here's the reality: if research has taken a backseat to clinical work, education is even further back, in the proverbial third row. Analogous to research work, academicians are not relegating educational efforts to the back burner maliciously. But the reality is there is not the money in lecturing to students and trainees, as there is in seeing patients and billing the insurance companies.

This is a critical aspect of the maladaptation of academic physicians because the success of the next generation of physicians hinges supremely on the efforts of today's professors. If they cannot engage in sufficient teaching in the best tradition of the university environment, due to pressures to see more patients and thereby become more productive, then it is not only today's students who ultimately suffer but, by extension, all citizens.

I remember many of my own professors fondly for their commitment to ensure my fellow students and I learned what was necessary to be the best physicians we could be. The head of our hematology/oncology program, a classical hematologist from Harvard, would pepper us with detailed questions of science and proper medical management. This would be at the multiple required educational conferences every week. Further education would consistently occur when seeing patients in the clinic or on hospital rounds. At times it would be stressful but with good reason: these are human lives being placed in our hands. And her goal unquestionably was to mold us into excellent doctors. At our conferences, all the other professors in the Hematology Division would attend and also participate actively in teaching us. One important element is that the other professors would always be present, both out of respect for our division chief and program director and also because she cultivated that culture of traditional didactic science and case discussion. By way of these efforts, we gradually grew more knowledgeable and confident and, at the conclusion of our fellowship training, felt extremely well-prepared to tackle the toughest cases. We were also proud to have gone through this academic rigor in our training. It felt like a very positively-intentioned rite of passage, and one with lasting professional benefits.

However, there are clear signs this academic tradition is fracturing. In speaking with colleagues who have been greatly involved with teaching, getting several professors to attend numerous educational conferences weekly is incredibly difficult nowadays. Greater time teaching means less time available to see patients, and the other doctors in that department are already under pressure to be sufficiently productive. Education slides down the list of priorities all too quickly. Ultimately, the success of such educational initiatives hinge largely on the sheer will of the professor tasked with these sessions. Colleagues I interviewed related to me that even with the best intentions and motivation, such efforts are hit or miss. Other physicians under pressure to be productive and go to their clinic are going to view teaching conferences as optional, when push comes to shove, just as our fictional Professor McMuffin felt. They simply don't feel compelled to attend.

In a medical training environment, the doctor spearheading education for students and trainees is typically the program director, referring to a residency program for instance. When faced with the equivalent of pulling teeth for her colleagues to come to and participate in conferences, the program director could consider turning to the university administration. However, if their objectives prioritize the clinical operations of the institution, then didactic discussions will probably take a back seat to seeing patients. The attitude received by some program directors is along the lines of "That's admirable and quaint, but there are bigger concerns."

Quite frankly, if program directors are not given enough protected time to teach medical science and discuss patient case management, then what will happen to the quality of preparation for the next generation of clinicians? Is it not our responsibility to ensure their readiness? I would like us to one day retire thinking securely that we are passing the torch to practiced and prepared hands. The alternative outcome, stemming from suboptimal educational activities, is both anxiety-provoking and one with widespread implications for the quality of healthcare delivery in America.

Therefore both the drain of physicians away from the research arena and the minimization of education in medical training are maladaptations of the academic doctor to the current healthcare environment in the United States. Dedicated research time is sacrificed for clinical work, driven by the business goals of their employers. Furthermore, if a budding research physician is unable to acquire adequate funding for his or her work, then this doctor may have little choice but to transition to engaging primarily in clinical work. The overwhelming majority of fiscally savvy hospitals are not going to have doctors drawing a typical salary for their field without sufficient work to justify such an income. Thus, if the researcher is unable to secure the requisite grants for their work, the administration may quite likely have the doctor see more patients instead. From the hospital's perspective, this is good practice; after all, they are not going to pay you without the commensurate productivity to show for it. However, from the perspective of the medical field, this is ultimately a negative because of the brain drain of smart doctors from scientific research.

The related maladaptation due to doctors being under pressure to see more patients and bill insurance companies also erodes the crucial cornerstone of medical education. This translates to potentially enormous intangible damage to valuable medical education for the next generation of doctors. Speaking as a physician, the general public benefits best from highly knowledgeable doctors who are steeped in an upbringing of deep analysis in concert with being educated by the top minds of the prior generation. I can vividly recall precious clinical nuances gained from my professors when they were teaching me and my classmates. Sometimes, entire presentations of how they explained central concepts burst into crystallized thought when pondering a clinical case. I cannot praise some of my own teachers enough, as the enormous rewards are still paying off years later.

Think about a favorite teacher in college or high school, and probably how well and enthusiastically you learned the subject matter as a result. To miss out on the full impact of what a great teacher can impart to their students, even if to a partial degree, is unquestionably an immense loss in my view. Again, bear in mind that this also feeds back into the next generation of doctors arguably not being able to treat the public as expertly. That is the most alarming consequence.

The other vital variable affecting an important fraction of academic physicians is the cost disconnect. Again, this is not a trivial issue. With the enormous costs of modern healthcare in America, it is essential that doctors, being on the front line with the patients, have to be educated on cost differences irrespective of where they practice. As discussed earlier, unfortunately there are many doctors who do not appreciate these enormous price variances for the same service, such as CT scans. It is not acceptable to hide behind the veneer of academia. It is, therefore, no shock that doctors in outpatient or independent practices will raise their hands in sheer astonishment whenever an academic doctor makes a head-shaking statement such as "I can treat the patient without worrying about cost." No, my colleague, you *must* keep costs and cost control at the forefront of your consideration for every patient!

The overarching question is "What is the primary mission of the academic hospital?" Is it about the advancement of medical science and education? Or is it to be a highly profitable institution? In modern-day healthcare, there are many administrative boards who feel it should be the latter, in that the entire operation must be first treated as a business and optimized as such. Now, if that is the case, that is an understandable and reasonable viewpoint.

However, it is both a loss for medical education and creates a leaky sieve for burgeoning physician-scientists. This ultimately is what leads to the chief disservice to the citizenry: there are nearly 1 million physicians in the United States, with most focused on clinical work.(98) The modern maladaptation of the academic physician is resulting in a loss for traditional research and teaching, and that is what carries profoundly unhealthy ramifications for the quality of scientific education for the next generation of doctors.

12

Pulse Check

Our patient rounds have finished for the day, but the patients have not been healed yet. Dr. Hippocrates, Professor McMuffin, Dr. Osler, and the others continue to face their significant fissiparous difficulties. Furthermore, these are just the seven individuals on *our ward*. Countless other doctors throughout the United States are confronting alarmingly similar tribulations. And the more doctors who find themselves at such professional crossroads translates to more of the public that cannot receive the best medical care. Their prognosis remains guarded, and the health of all citizens is at stake.

The American healthcare system is a calamitous combination of massively expensive tests and therapies, insurance companies determining patients' treatments, and sprawling hospital systems making billions in revenue. Without question, it stands to reason that health insurance corporations funding over $2.5 trillion in medical costs effectively grants these insurers control of what treatments will be reimbursed or not. Both the physician's consultation time and treatment costs are not determined by market forces but, rather, by contracted rates with insurance corporations, which has fundamentally changed the delivery of medical care in the last few decades.

But the downstream effects have flowed far deeper than monetary concerns and how we possibly can fund our grotesquely expensive healthcare system. The potent forces that have been unleashed have led to several types of doctors that, in spite of their best efforts, have not been able to adjust well to the current conditions in US healthcare. These doctors have maladapted to this aberrant system, and consequently, doctors themselves are changing radically, and for the worse. This is truly the equivalent of an earthquake shaking the sacred patient-doctor relationship to its core.

My goal in illustrating these types of doctors is not at all to criticize my fellow physicians but, rather, to show the current reality that has materialized as a *result* of this fractured system. The dedicated, caring, house-call doctor is but a rosy memory for almost all of the American public. This is not because doctors of the current era do not care enough. Rather, career decisions, changing styles of practice, and the pursuit of nontraditional medical careers are all maladaptations to the broken system as a whole.

The various types of doctors that have emerged are ones I have personally encountered and fastidiously observed, as have numerous colleagues of mine across the nation. The "Idealistic Doctor" becoming increasingly frustrated, burning out, and changing jobs. The "Hospital-Employed Doctor" never receiving appreciation for his work, gradually losing motivation, coupled with an outsized emphasis on patient satisfaction surveys. The "Wealthy Doctor", though brilliant and well-published in the medical literature, now giving cosmetic Botox shots for cash while eschewing Medicare. The "Professor" being forced to do more and more clinic work and less time teaching future doctors.

I assure you these are professional scenarios that virtually no one imagined when studying in medical school a couple decades ago or more. Phenomena such as burnout are pervasive in the medical profession today and are yet another ruinous ramification of the fractured US healthcare system. Is it any wonder that increasing numbers of doctors are exiting to nontraditional medical careers? The overwhelming majority of doctors feel they cannot reconcile their medical training with the malfunctioning system, so they either throw their hands in the air and put up with the cavalcade of problems (or as we have discussed, *maladapt*) or switch to another job or career option.

When doctors branch out to circumvent these systemic troubles by, for example, administering botulinum toxin injections, as our fictional Dr. Phillips did, they can truly escape some of the problems. For example, if Dr. Phillips saw mostly Medicare-insured dermatology patients instead of either cash-paying or those with commercial insurance plans, he would stand to take a considerable income cut. Therefore by offering cosmetic injections and the like, he is able to flee from insurance denials and reimbursement frustrations and, thereby, maintain both his income level and professional independence. The latter factor, that of professional independence, means a great deal to many doctors. Small business owners can relate to this feeling.

Several of the maladaptations we have discussed, such as adding cosmetic offerings like Dr. Phillips did, may actually work out quite well for the individual physician. The need for the highly educated, intelligent, well-published dermatologist to engage in these nontraditional medical practices is fundamentally fueled by the insurance climate and other systemic problems in medicine. In addition, there is a multibillion-dollar market for these offerings, and thus many in the public are seeking such services.(62) Once the doctor is presenting such services, sure, he or she may not be curing skin cancer, but he's making a good income and many people are getting what they want.

However, this departure from mainstream medical practice is ultimately a loss for the general public. How about those skin cancer patients who are on Medicare? Well, it becomes someone else's problem. After all, there are other dermatologists out there, right? But the pool is dwindling. This is why these maladaptations result in a brain drain. Many of the top scientific, entrepreneurial, and creative minds in medicine are branching out to literally escape the problems of the system. Also recall what we discussed in an earlier chapter: with the market opportunity along with the backdrop of insurance problems such as denials and reduced reimbursement, other doctors beyond dermatologists are aspiring for their piece of the pie and getting involved with cosmetic offerings. I have seen not only numerous primary care physicians but even a pulmonologist (lung specialist) engaging in these "superficial" services! Thus it is a loss for both those skin cancer patients and the general public's standard of medical care as a whole.

In the United States, we have a vast network of elite medical institutions and access to virtually any therapy. But with trillions of dollars at stake in the healthcare sector, medicine in America has become a game of insurance companies, costly therapies, and who can get contracts sufficient for sustaining business. This is fundamentally why large hospital and clinic systems are dominating outpatient medical care in so many communities in the nation. It is not their fault to have taken advantage of this environment, but they have the clout to obtain strong contracts with health insurers and the money to purchase innumerable outpatient clinics into their respective systems. If you have more patients under your proverbial umbrella, that is more money you can bill to an insurance company, and ultimately huge amounts of money the system will receive for their services. For large systems, this leads to revenues in the *billions* annually.

It is the patient—and so the general public—who is increasingly paying for this. The out-of-pocket deductible for the average American family is over $4,000.(8) Remember, that $4,000 is in addition to your monthly bill for the insurance premium. Meanwhile, with this backdrop, standard services such as X-rays and CT scans will cost much more to have in a hospital facility than a physician's office or other independent radiology facility. To clarify, when a patient is sent for such a study to a hospital facility, I am referring to an *outpatient* study at a hospital-owned location; coverage for an inpatient is handled differently. For an echocardiogram, this can often be double the cost in a hospital clinic versus a cardiologist's office.(7)

Again, you are being charged more for the *exact same service*! Furthermore, the patient increasingly foots the extra bill, courtesy of higher insurance deductible costs over recent years.(8) This is known as cost-shifting.

Now, you'll see advertising from these glitzy, costly facilities with claims about why you want to get a standard X-ray or CT scan done there instead of a more affordable place. But don't fall for the marketing hype. For the overwhelming fraction of standard X-rays and the like, any trained board-certified radiologist can properly interpret the scan. Moreover, the CT or MRI machine is neither unique nor manufactured by the hospital; they are sold to them by companies like Siemens, who sell to thousands of other clinics across the country and world.

The trillions of dollars flowing from patients to health insurance companies, and then downstream to sprawling, large clinic systems, is not a salubrious dynamic for American health*care*. Innumerable excellent doctors are leaving traditional medical practice, exasperated by the current medical system. Is this what we truly want? Corporate-style medical offices, inflated charges, additional facility fees, and insurance companies deciding what diabetes medication you should take instead of your physician?

13

Persistent Symptoms

I n medicine, very typically it is the chronic diagnoses that are the toughest to solve. Patients often have to grapple with symptoms for years, or even indefinitely. It is often a protracted journey, featuring low points interspersed with occasional rays of sunshine. These glimpses of hope are ones that doctors ask patients to look toward, as they may indicate that hint of breakthroughs and better times ahead.

Quite similarly, it is the systemic problems baked into the medical system over the last few decades, that have twisted the course of American healthcare down an arduous path. The potent negative forces have stressed the medical system to the point that the very heart of medical care—the doctor-patient relationship—is under attack. The exorbitant costs, heft of sizable and expanding hospital corporations, and control of health insurance companies has now filtered down to fracturing doctors into pathologic styles of practice. This is an entangled problem that simply does not have a plainly apparent solution.

As the situation is presently, doctors cannot readily thrust the healthcare system onto a more virtuous path. Contemplate the dilemma our fictional Dr. Bill Osler, the idealistic physician, faces. He enthusiastically set out to dispense the very best care and treatment medical science knows. While highly educated and well-trained, he was unfortunately not equipped with the real-world skills necessary to tackle insurance denials, high patient copays, and battling the system in general. This is a dramatic shortcoming of medical training, which focuses so heavily on the science; this focus is necessary but not sufficient for navigating the healthcare landscape today.

Dr. Osler and innumerable idealistic-minded physicians across the nation are ultimately at the mercy of the dysfunctional medical system. They possess few realistic options to salvage their personal situation. One can continue fighting and run the significant hazard of burnout and disillusionment. Alternatively, they can find a job at another clinic. However, certain challenges from the system will continue regardless of location (within the US). Importantly, a doctor changing jobs also breaks the continuity of care for patients—the patient loses their doctor, and they have to essentially start from scratch with someone else. Thirdly, physicians at such crossroads can exit clinical medicine by seeking a nontraditional career, such as in pharmaceutical research.

Among these options, a frequent career move is to change jobs. This is redolent with the idea and hope of "the grass is greener on the other side of the fence," as a large set of challenges in the previous job are actually a reflection of the systemic problems in healthcare and not isolated to one clinic. Therefore, the frustration and fatigue from spending 40–50% of the working day with your electronic medical record software, for example, will likely rear its head again quickly in the new position. Doctors moving to a new clinic, termed "physician turnover", is a colossal problem. Again, it is a maladaptation by the physician, as he or she feels they have simply had enough and cannot conceivably function in their workplace without an intolerable level of dissatisfaction.

In line with the maladapting theme, it is ultimately the patients who lose out the most from turnover. In my field of hematology and oncology, I see a large number of complex patients who require subspecialty care and guidance. These admirable patients, commonly bearing symptoms of their conditions chronically, have had the subtleties of their diagnosis managed by the same doctor for years, if not over a decade. Thus, if the patient finds their doctor has moved to a new clinic, unless it is nearby, they often have lost their subspecialist and have to locate a new one.

Patients with complicated cases feature many intricate nuances. When the doctor leaves for another clinic (maybe even another state), the patient will have to essentially reinvent the wheel. Going through the medical details with a new doctor is hard enough, and additionally, there is the intangible of hoping to build a rapport such that the patient is happy with their new doctor. As anyone who has been through this can attest, discovering the right match is far from a given.

This unfortunate phenomenon is not restricted to subspecialists and complex cases. Primary care physicians regularly have to effectively monitor and treat multiple diagnoses, and they have a startlingly high amount of turnover also. In one study examining 740 primary care clinicians in California, a whopping 30% no longer worked in the same clinic or system three years later.(99) Consider: nearly a third of clinicians have moved on in only three years! If you have a chronic diagnosis or multiple diagnoses and have to reset with a new doctor every three years, that is light-years away from being a desirable situation. In the medical sphere, this is referred to as a break in the continuity of care. To me, as a physician, this bewildering high turnover is simply not an acceptable state of affairs.

In the aforementioned study, the same trends were found to be present for physician assistants and nurse practitioners. In addition, the clinical staff (referring to nurses, medical assistants, and so forth) had a turnover fraction of a stunning 41%.(99) This study found a correlation of burnout as a significant predictor of job change: there was a 57% relatively higher chance of clinician turnover if they were suffering from burnout as well. It is worth reiterating that the mechanisms present today to screen for or mitigate burnout are woefully ineffective, if not barely existent.

In my experience, I have not heard a single person among the hospital or department leadership *ever* ask me about how I was handling job stress, over many years. You'll see an occasional email about it to the medical staff, with links to online "resources." But that is a preposterous substitute for something more specific like a conversation. Bear in mind, I am a cancer specialist, where life and death is an all too real part of the job.

In an earlier chapter, I referenced a book written by an obstetrician and gynecologist in the United Kingdom, Dr. Adam Kay.(61) Recall that he wrote about how he made a radical career change to comedic script writing due to the disturbing, stressful experiences he had in medicine, and how it affected his morale and personal life. Doctors are clearly not immune to stress and burnout like any other human being. (24, 25) But this dovetails into job turnover and a loss of continuity of care for patients. This translates into suboptimal medical care for a patient, and this is where it is not "just" the doctor's problem but a phenomenon that has real-world consequences for the health of the public!

Thus, one may be a highly educated and well-intentioned doctor, with the best interests of the patient at heart, but in today's healthcare environment it often just is not enough. With insurance companies overriding a doctor's data-driven treatment preference, burnout, and job turnover happening distressingly often, this simply is not a recipe for best patient care.

Our fictional Dr. Osler, the first patient on our ward, had to confront the aforementioned problems. Meanwhile, the last patient we saw, Professor McMuffin, also touched on something highly disconcerting: the erosion of medical education.

From my vantage point, it is a colossal problem that rigorous medical education is falling down in the list of priorities in the healthcare sphere. This spawns a vast array of consequences, centered around the next generation of medical students not being taught as consistently by the best professors. A strong didactic education, juxtaposed with real world clinical cases, is essential in one's quest to be the best doctor possible. This ensures a high standard among the graduates. Therefore, the professors remaining reliably involved and having sufficient protected time to teach serves as a quality control mechanism for medical trainees. This engagement simultaneously can make them compelling role models for the next generation. This quality standard is a necessity: after all, this is our collective health and lives we are talking about. Almost nothing else has this level of importance, other than perhaps one's spiritual or religious beliefs.

I vividly recall lectures by certain professors, particularly in the specific manner by which they explained a diagnosis or treatment. In the field of oncology, sifting through the details of a cancer diagnosis with a patient and their family involves a multifaceted discussion involving the prognosis, the pros and cons of therapies, and, crucially, understanding the patient's personal perspectives and wishes. With such complexities, you really need to have a proper framework in mind. And that's exactly what these phenomenal teachers imparted upon my classmates and colleagues, over twenty years ago. It is these golden nuggets that make a precious indelible mark on students, and this can make all the difference in the world when human lives are at stake. Therefore we, as physicians, need to "pay it forward"; however, as occurred with Professor McMuffin, this ability is hampered markedly by lack of time and education being a lower priority in a modern medical facility. Simply reading the textbooks and taking examinations does not automatically make one a great doctor.

I remember one of my favorite rotations in residency training, in the leukemia ward. My professor was one of the smartest physicians I know, and had a fantastic ability to connect with patients. We were all working intensely every day, seeing 30 critically ill patients on the ward with life-threatening diseases, discussing complicated medical conundrums. In the midst of this strenuous clinical work, our professor would make sure we set aside time for educational discussion. This struck me as completing the circle in terms of connecting the textbooks with the practical application.

One day on this rotation, without warning, after several days of both learning and treating patients, I was asked by my professor to explain treatment options to a patient with newly diagnosed acute leukemia. He essentially wanted to test my knowledge in a real-world situation, in the tradition of good medical education. It was somewhat stressful to suddenly discuss something both so serious and also with your professor watching you. However, I felt prepared due to the combination of the clinical (patient) experience in addition to having observed my professor impart the same type of discussion to multiple patients before.

Alas, times have changed. The emphasis conveyed by many institutions to their medical staff is to prioritize clinical work and billing. Flexibility in the schedule to teach and critically assess science is at a high premium. I feel that, on one hand, one cannot blame the hospital system's focus (or that of any large, corporate clinic organization) on maximizing billing: firstly, they are providing these services, and secondly, this strategy is amplifying the financial success of the organization as a whole. However, with a limited amount of time and energy in the day, medical education takes a backseat. Doctors thereby lose huge fractions of their protected time for lecturing and related activities. Long-time colleagues of mine have related to me how they have to push tirelessly to keep adequate teaching time on the agenda and also how they have to almost beg other doctors to tear away from clinical duties and participate in teaching. Ultimately, teaching does not fatten the bottom line.

I believe the consequences of this are dire. Again, memorizing the textbooks does not magically make one into a strong clinician. We need the guidance, perspective, experience, and nuances of the real-world expressed to us when doctors are going through schooling and residency training. Furthermore, the best teachers convey these intangibles, along with being quintessential role models.

Perhaps the ultimate irony is that the word "doctor" originates from the Latin for "teacher"! To me it is highly worrisome that the quality of future clinicians is what potentially suffers. This is a titanic problem that needs to be thoroughly addressed.

Ultimately, all of the maladaptations by our seven types of doctors are a loss for the medical care of the public. When a doctor leaves traditional medicine and segues into research, consulting, or even news media, it is unmistakably a loss for the countless patients who could have benefited from her expertise. It is quintessentially a brain drain.

Therein lies the enormity of the problem. Does not every single patient wish, when they have a heart condition, for instance, that the cardiologist is experienced, caring, and well-trained? Is there anyone who is honestly hoping that a more "average" cardiologist is going to be treating them? Thus the doctor-patient relationship is under a withering assault. For the sake of our collective health, this is not acceptable!

To me, this is a call to action for the American people. Do we not want the brightest scientific minds and caring individuals to be our physicians? If so, the critical ballasts of regional hospital monopolies, costly procedures, expensive therapies, and insurance control have to materially change. However, the sweeping polarization in the current political climate makes me pessimistic about a near-term viable solution. But perhaps like investment markets, opportunities and creative solutions will sometimes be discovered when there is a prevailing pessimism.

14

TREATMENT OPTIONS

I n an article in the *Journal of the American Medical Association* authored by Dr. Thomas Shwenk, dean of the school of medicine at the University of Nevada, Reno, he remarked that the "expensive and wasteful US health care system has caused private and government payers to burden physicians with a wide range of regulatory, financial, and productivity pressures that conflict with or are antithetical to fundamental professional responsibilities."(100) Therefore, the changes of the system are wounding what it means to be a physician and eroding the integrity of the core job of a physician. As a result, we have seen a vast array of maladaptations that doctors have made, which is ultimately damaging the sacred doctor-patient relationship and consequently the healthcare of all Americans.

Thus we have reached this point. The considerable problems in the healthcare sphere have filtered down to fracturing doctors into pathologic styles of practice. Part and parcel with this, the heart of medical care, the doctor-patient relationship, is under duress. For these fundamental reasons, these problems gravely impact us all.

What we can do to rehabilitate these problems is astonishingly complex. I do not profess to have a simple or secret answer. However, I can posit a number of elements that may eventually contribute to the solution—or at least foster change in the right direction. The situation is not immutable.

The forthcoming variables are the sine qua non of the "treatment" for our complicated predicament. We've seen these manifest in varied forms in terms of how they affected our seven types of doctors. Just as these issues forced our doctors to change for the worse, these have to also be rectified to set us back onto the right path. Bear in mind that these variables take time to develop in terms of real-world application. We may not immediately find ourselves on a yellow brick road, but we'll be moving closer.

First on the list is addressing regulation of the ever-growing large medical institutions popping up in local markets across the United States. This is, effectively, one type of monopoly regulation. Like previously discussed, on one hand, it is quite understandable that these corporations are striving to optimize profit. Their priority is to prosper in the business environment of the healthcare sector. Moreover, many institutions are doing this successfully to the tune of billions of dollars in gross profit. Hospitals, for instance, account for approximately 50% of healthcare spending in the US, and these costs are growing at about 5% per year.(96) In addition, a staggering $1 trillion flows from health insurance companies to hospital corporations across the nation.(2)

Over the past several years, hospital systems have grown by buying out doctors and private practices and absorbing them into their corporate umbrellas. The goal of the major hospital in your local area is to maximize the number of patients getting services through that system. Traditionally, hospitals were predominantly for inpatient care, but now they have aggressively bolstered outpatient services.

More patients means more evaluations, procedures, and treatments, which results in more revenue. The net effect of this is that patient choice diminishes. Before, in relatively more rural areas, whereas before local residents had at least a few albeit limited healthcare options, now there often is literally just one institution. This further drives up prices of all healthcare services provided by that institution: doctor visits at the hospital-owned clinics, CT scans and other radiology scans, medicines dispensed at the hospital pharmacy, and procedures. Large medical organizations already hold more lucrative contracts with health insurance companies—that is, getting more money for the same service provided—and once they are the only game in town, they can raise prices further. At the end of the day, the patient pays.

Again, increasing profitability is the goal of any corporation; that is not improper. But akin to any industry, it is within the government's purview that this growth does not impinge upon competition, patient choice, and reasonability of cost. In my view, the US economy benefits from a flourishing healthcare sector. At the same time, these key variables of consumer choice and cost have to be adequately monitored, particularly when this is a trillion-dollar sector.

Therefore the effort for pricing transparency that has been proposed by the US federal government in November 2019 is a vital piece of the puzzle to rein in these costs. Large swaths of the public are only peripherally aware that they have to pay much more for the exact same CT scan at a hospital-owned radiology facility than a free-standing or private location. As we've discussed, you may get charged double for an echocardiogram in a hospital clinic versus a cardiologist's office.(7) Similarly, cancer chemotherapy and other treatments may cost a few multiples more. Part of this will be covered by your health insurance—but with ever-rising deductible and monthly premium expenses, proportionally more has to be forked over by you, the patient.

Pricing transparency is a key aspect of controlling such costs. The other piece of this is improved oversight by the state and federal level to regulate potentially monopolistic practices. The dynamics can vary widely depending on the particular local market being analyzed. After all, in some localities where sizeable institutions may be present, there may still be adequate competition. However, in those regions where a critical mass of independent practices are bought out by large institutions, or perhaps where a merger has been completed between the only two health conglomerates in the area, governmental oversight is critical. The government's responsibility is to ensure that consumers still have sufficient choice and costs for services are not suddenly skyrocketing.

We see that patient choice can become restricted and costs rise markedly as large clinic organizations take over healthcare in your local market. Patient choice can be negatively impacted from another angle as well: that of the conscience-based objection. Religiously affiliated hospitals comprise roughly 25% of US hospitals.(103) Apparently, under current law, hospitals can refuse medical care on the "basis of their religious, moral, ethical, or other convictions."(104) Historically, such objections had to do with issues around abortions and contraception, but the rights of "entities" (i.e., corporations) have more recently been expanded. Now the scope of medical options that can be denied includes mental health services, child abuse services, and vaccines. A hospital can even object on "conscience" grounds to treating those of different sexual orientations.(103) The authors of an article in the *New England Journal of Medicine* further state that these circumstances "encroach on patients' rights and access by diminishing choice and transparency" and call upon "state regulators to assess proposed mergers" to see if they will "adversely affect the communities that the merging hospitals serve."(103)

This concept of conscience-based objection by an organization is fascinating, and it underscores the point at hand. When the doctor is an employee, you essentially have to follow the company's party line or find another job. If the employer is implementing policies driven by ethical or religious convictions, they do not care about the doctor's years of experience, how well-trained he or she may be, or how medically valid a concern may be. Hence, adequate regulation and competition in all markets is indispensable to decrease the chance of such situations controlling patient choice.

From a physician's perspective, this is alarming to me from another level also: the possible loss of autonomy in terms of advocating for patients. An absolutely central component of a physician's ethos is to act in accordance with the best interests of the patient. From that sense, this manifested during the coronavirus (SARS-CoV-2) pandemic of 2019–2020 originating from Wuhan, China. There were multiple instances of doctors and nurses allegedly muzzled from speaking up about concerns about the lack of adequate infection protection (e.g., masks, gloves, gowns, etc.) for the medical staff and patients.(101) The diminishment of patient advocacy is definitely not a slippery slope we want to step upon.

Naturally, communities need hospitals for *inpatient care* and select procedures. However, the current situation, with sprawling healthcare institutions taking over local markets, is laden with a frenzy of downstream effects on medical practice that we have explored in this book. With hospitals accounting for over $1 trillion in healthcare expenditures annually, pricing transparency along with governmental oversight to ensure consumer choice and prevent monopolistic practices is sorely needed. Additionally, doctors and nurses need to be able to advocate freely for the best interests of their patients, and simultaneously patient rights cannot be curtailed. These steps are achievable. Supported by a framework of enforceable laws, these measures have the potential to catalyze competition and lower prices across the country.

Next on the prescription for these systemic problems is how doctors can meaningfully shift from their dependence on health insurance. Perhaps the most severe stressor and common thread affecting our seven doctors is how insurance companies are dictating medical care. We saw how our fictional Dr. Osler tried to prescribe the blood pressure medication with the best evidence from clinical studies, only to be rebuffed by the insurance company. He had to try the older, less-effective medication first by the patient's insurance company's decision. Does any patient in America go to their doctor to get the second-best medication for their condition?

Another example is in diabetes treatment, where there has been great progress with new therapies that go beyond the old paradigm of either insulin injections or oral medications that originated from 25 years ago or more. One shining example of this research is using a new class of medications to stimulate a pathway in the body known as glucagon-like peptide 1 (GLP-1). When someone eats food containing glucose (sugar or carbohydrates), GLP-1 is one of the hormones that regulates your pancreas gland to secrete insulin. The class of medicines that have been successfully developed to work on this pathway are known as GLP-1 receptor agonists, and they have excellent data in enhancing control of diabetes and are even being associated with weight loss.

However, on some health insurance plans, it is astoundingly difficult to have GLP-1 pathway medications approved. It does not matter if you are a board-certified fellowship-trained endocrinologist or not; the insurance company is deciding your treatment. Instead the patient has to try and "fail" other older medications first (believe it or not the insurance forms will ask if the patient has failed the insurance-mandated number of medications when requesting a GLP-1 agonist). Alternatively, the copay for the GLP-1 agonist will be prohibitively high, and most patients simply cannot afford the therapy with the better evidence.

On this issue, doctors and patients are completely aligned; the patient deserves the best treatment for their condition. Yes, the physician can attempt to scale the uphill climb against the insurance corporation to overturn their decision, such as by initiating an appeal with the company. However, in the current landscape of practice, this is practically difficult to pull off consistently. Such appeals will be within the precious minutes doctors have between the other 25 patients they have to see that day—due to the ever-declining insurance reimbursement for the doctor's hard work.

Some doctors will, therefore, make the maladaptation of alternative income streams such as offering cosmetic injections, as our "patient" Dr. Ozzie Phillips did. However, other options are arising from the carnage of modern healthcare, including ways for the doctor to even stay engaged with traditional medical practice, in a sense. One such model is known as "Direct Primary Care", or DPC.

Under the framework of Direct Primary Care, the core approach is centered on high-quality patient care, extended appointment time with your doctor, minimizing financial barriers, and easy accessibility to one's doctor, including by phone and email. With this model, the doctor does not accept health insurance plans. Instead, patients are part of the doctor's practice under a retainer or subscription model. Patients pay a flat monthly fee to the practice, amounting typically to around $50–100. In return, patients receive a much-enhanced level of service with their physician. Per the American Academy of Family Physicians (AAFP), the advantages include "real time access via advanced communication technology to their personal physician, extended visits, in some cases home-based medical visits, and highly personalized, coordinated, and comprehensive care administration."(105)

With direct primary care, patients benefit from both greater quantity of time and quality care with the physician. The "quantity" is manifested by much more time at your appointments. I have several colleagues that will allocate 30–60 minutes per appointment, depending on the nature of the concern. This is, of course, a radical contrast to the typical five to seven minutes per visit with many insurance-dependent practices. In the latter situation, due to diminishing insurance payments, the doctor has to see 20–30 patients per day just to be able to pay the overhead and maintain his level of income. However, with DPC, the physician does not bear the pressure of seeing a certain threshold of patients every day, as he already feels he is being compensated fairly for his services via the monthly "subscription." Having only 7–10 patients for the entire day, for example, equates to each patient being able to be seen for the time they truly need, as the doctor is not mired in health insurance obstacles and paperwork in between.

Secondly, as a patient with DPC, you can have unlimited appointments at no extra charge. For the diabetic patient who needs close monitoring of his insulin regimen, or the stroke patient struggling through his recovery who desires more frequent medical evaluations, this is easily accomplished through the retainer model of DPC. Even phone calls and emails are readily feasible, as the doctor has more time. When one is contracted with health insurances, however, a phone call is unpaid or "nonreimbursed" time out of the hectic schedule, and hence, the doctor is disincentivized to engage in this extra communication.

In addition to the upgraded quantity of service you receive, the quality also rockets upward. Firstly, doctors can treat patients as they feel is best, based on their medical experience and the latest literature. This is a huge plus point. Furthermore, they are not affected by insurance company decisions as to how many times a patient can see the doctor and for how long, for instance. You do not have to worry about your appointment not being covered by the insurance plan just because you went to the office two weeks ago. Secondly, as the doctor feels she is getting paid fairly for her services, there is decreased incentive to venture into ancillary services such as cosmetic shots. Therefore, more physicians will focus on what they were trained to do: bread and butter medical care. This greater focus directly benefits you as the patient.

A pleasing byproduct of the doctor having to see fewer patients is that she *knows you better*. It is easier for the physician to keep track of key nuances that can sometimes result in a vital decision aiding the patient's health. This is a subtle but salient point. To provide a sense of what this means on a practice level, consider that in an average insurance-dependent primary care practice in the US, there are about 4,000 patients. Conversely in a direct primary care practice, it is estimated that there are 800–1,000 patients.(106) Therefore, with DPC, if every patient came four times a year (subtracting out weekends), that sums to about 13 patients a day. In my experience, virtually all physicians will state that 10–13 patients a day is very manageable and simultaneously have confidence that the quality of care will be quite high.

There are now over 1,000 direct primary care practices in the United States.(107) Doctors have gravitated strongly toward the numerous advantages for both the patient and for themselves. There are even other additional advantages, including the DPC model allowing the practice to keep the overhead low. Insurance-dependent practices have to have employees specifically hired (or alternatively hire outsourced third-party companies) to check insurance "eligibility" (i.e., is the doctor in the patient's insurance network), as well as people to submit reimbursement claims, fight insurance denials, and keep track of what reimbursement has been received by the practice or not. This whole component of the practice is clearly not cheap. But circumventing expenses such as these, this aggregates to enormous savings over time for medical practices.

Beyond the cost savings, gains may be realized in the risk of burnout. Consider that physicians have historically always been one of the highest-risk groups for burnout, courtesy of the emotional and psychological toll of caring for sick and dying human beings.(19) This threat to professional longevity is running much hotter on account of the heavy headwinds of the current era: minimal time per patient, a decrease in income stemming from worsening insurance reimbursement, and innumerable logistical barriers in daily practice. Undoubtedly, each of these forces are much lessened with models like direct primary care. Doctors can spend dramatically more time with patients while not worrying about either insurance companies paying for a patient visit, or the daily fighting with paperwork and denials. This brew of less burnout, greater professional satisfaction and time with patients has the right ingredients to allow doctors to be at their best and, thus, deliver top-quality medical care. That's what ultimately matters, no?

While direct primary care features a multitude of plus points that can facilitate transforming medical practice, there are a few aspects that hold it back from being ubiquitously applied across America. Firstly, because DPC typically only includes treatment from your primary care physician, most patients will also need some form of limited health insurance to cover hospital visits and specialist treatments. Such policy options are commonly known as "catastrophic health insurance", and fortunately they are far lower than the cost of a comprehensive health insurance policy. Secondly, if you take several medications, you will want prescription drug insurance as well. Pharmaceutical drug expenditures continue to be dwarfed by hospital-incurred costs in the US; in 2016, medication expenses reflected 10% of the total cost.(2) Still, for an individual patient on multiple medications, drug costs can run a few hundred dollars per month.

A third drawback to wide application of DPC is that it will be more difficult to roll out this model in lower economic zones. In spite of the upside of markedly upgraded medical care by your personal physician, for the financially less well-off patient, paying $50–100 per month simply may not be an option. Still, even if a direct primary care practice cannot open up on every street corner in America, the overall positives are significant. High-quality medicine, much more time with your doctor, and elimination of insurance whims dictating your healthcare are crucial variables we need in place for the betterment of the system.

The next essential element that needs to be reformed is the electronic health record system. Perhaps one of the most shocking statistics we have reviewed is that physicians spend several hours, and about 50% of their working day, in front of EHRs.(20) More time clicking away at computers with bloated software, foremost, means less time with a patient! As a corollary, more data entered into a computer does *not* somehow create better medical care either. As Dr. Thomas Schwenk wrote in the *Journal of the American Medical Association* in 2020, physicians are spending substantial time to "support clinical documentation systems [EHRs] that meet business and legal needs but have limited clinical value."(100)

Time spent with electronic health record systems has to be chopped down. The doctor needs to be freer to invest time in patient care, firstly by having more time to talk with patients. This investment also includes having extra time to think about a case, as well as being able to research further with medical journals when necessary.

While medical documentation, or writing notes in a patient's chart, has long been needed for legal reasons, it has also become necessary for billing insurance companies. A labyrinthine array of numerical codes have to be submitted to Medicare and other health insurance companies. Then, to justify a specific code, voluminous data points need to be entered into the chart. In other words, if sufficient data is not recorded, the doctor may not get reimbursed for the service given! You may instead get paid a lesser amount; this hit to the reimbursement is typically about 25% or more. This can coalesce into sizeable sums over the course of a year.

The above should give the reader a good sense of why approximately 50% of a physician's workday is spent in front of a computer, but allow me to elaborate further. With the troves of data that are collated in electronic medical record systems, particularly those at larger hospitals and emergency departments, the number of pages of information recorded is just incredible. When I get a report from a patient having visited the emergency department, for example, customarily I receive records totaling *20 to 30 pages*. Upon receipt, I have to search through this novella to find just the one or two paragraphs of information that is actually useful! Foremost, I am hunting for something theoretically simple: what was the ER doctor's clinical impression or conclusion. The remainder of the information contained in the dozens of computer-generated pages may help in billing the insurance company, but from a medical decision-making perspective, it is extraneous. It is laughably outrageous how difficult this search is; ask any physician friend you have, and I bet they will echo the same experience.

On account of this rapidly expanding balloon of EHR medical charting, in conjunction with the amount of time lost to a computer and away from the patient, deep changes are necessary to the documentation process. Principally, we have to streamline the data entry process. Cranking out literally reams of pages while spending half of your workday in front of computers is harmful to good medical practice. We saw what our fictional older patient, Dr. Hippocrates, experienced: frustration along with struggling to adapt to complex medical programs for clinical documentation. He found it extraordinarily difficult to meld spending hours with the computer with properly utilizing his decades of medical experience of how to best help patients. Therefore, the data entry, whether for documenting the rationale of a treatment or to support insurance billing, has to be dramatically more succinct.

Perhaps this is a real business opportunity for manufacturers of EHR systems. Previous research investigating the factors causing frustration with EHRs chiefly discovered the following: remembering menu and button names and commands use, performing tasks that are not straightforward, system speed, and system reliability.[21] The aforementioned variables have the common thread of all being features that affect real-time usability. For the doctor working a long day in the clinic, a computer system needs to be fast, easy to use and carry the ability to smoothly document enough about the patient visit for medical, legal, and billing reasons. Furthermore, the patient visit note should not result in 30 pages being faxed to a colleague. Beyond that, all the fancy graphics plus other bells and whistles ultimately do not matter.

This data should hopefully be edifying for EHR companies aiming to appeal to more doctors. The driving philosophy is that we should be greatly minimizing time with the EHR and maximizing time with the patient. This does not minimize the value of an electronic system compared to old paper charts, but hugely enhanced time-efficiency is required. Billing cannot be the top priority under this supposition. Obviously, getting paid adequately for services provided is a must, but I believe sufficient billing will follow organically if the EHR systems are upgraded with this philosophy in mind.

As mentioned previously, beyond the practical usability improvements sorely needed, the documentation for billing insurance companies needs to be streamlined. For example, among primary care physicians, 90% of follow-up patient appointments are billed under two specific codes: 99213 and 99214. (108, 109) Knowing the high frequency of using two codes, chart notes in an EHR can potentially be autopopulated with all the elements to satisfy documentation for one of these two codes. (Note that coding is more diverse for other fields such as surgery and oncology.) Under this construct, the doctor receives the choice of either 99213, 99214, or "other." If she selects one of the first two options (which is the case 90% of the time), the note opens and is autopopulated with all the elements needed, including the billing code. Then the doctor can quickly address just those points she needs to modify. In my experience, this may be less than five variables, and perhaps as few as three. After this, she signs the note, and the documentation has been rapidly completed. (See Figure 4 for a proposed flowchart.)

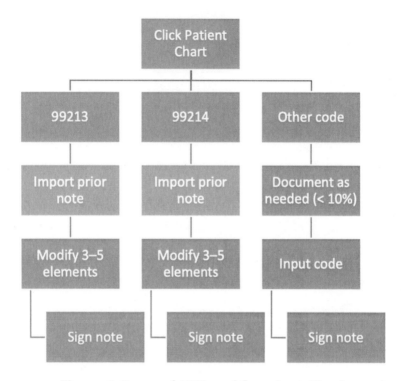

Figure 4. Proposed EHR workflow chart. Blue boxes denote points when the clinician has to input or modify data. Gray boxes denote autopopulated steps completed by the software. The final green boxes are when the clinician clicks to finish/sign a note.

The electronic system ought to be a useful tool facilitating medical care. Instead, as it stands today, medical care is increasingly being subsumed by the EHR system! Let me also propose a target goal for EHR developers: a clinician should be able to complete every patient's chart note in three minutes or less. And we need to hear that this target is reliably achievable directly from practicing doctors, and not just from technology companies. Consequently, if one saw 20 patients, only one hour is spent out of the day on patient charting. (Note that clinicians also have to sift through dozens of lab results, radiology documents, and messages—so wrapping up charting does not finish all computer work.) Bear in mind why these endeavors to attain greater simplicity are needed: electronic systems have become decidedly more complex for insurance billing and reimbursement purposes, and this is detracting considerable time from best patient care.

One path circumventing many insurance reimbursement obstacles are methods such as installing the direct primary care model. Another method is to connect monitoring a set of clinical characteristics, or "quality" metrics, to determine reimbursement. In other words, if the patient with diabetes has better sugar control, the medical office gets paid more. Similarly, prescribing certain standard medications, such as particular classes of blood pressure medicines for diabetics, will garner a check in the list of metrics.

So-called quality metrics sound good in theory, but are problematic in the real world. Firstly, control of specific clinical measurements can be affected by forces beyond the control of the doctor, such as if the diabetic individual decides to eat two doughnuts with breakfast every morning. Secondly, these metric programs often involve a litany of measurements to sort through, which can be logistically burdensome to collate.(112) Thirdly, prescription medications may not be so easily affordable for patients. Success of attaining these health outcome goals also hinges on socioeconomics. The wealthy suburb will have proportionally more residents able to afford the nutritious salad, Greek yogurt, and to retain a gym membership. Is it any wonder they will have better blood sugar results?

On this clash of theory meets reality, Dr. Seema Verma, who headed the Centers for Medicare & Medicaid Services (CMS) beginning in 2017 said, "We need to move from fee-for-service to a system that pays for value and quality—

but how we define value and quality today is a problem . . .
Moreover, it's not clear whether all of these measures are
actually improving patient care."(110)

Meanwhile, Dr. Jerry Penso, the chief executive officer of
the American Medical Group Association, a large advocacy
group representing nearly 200,000 physicians nationwide,
urged simplicity. In a campaign involving 150 medical
groups, a focus on just four metrics "improved care for 1 in
3 patients in the first year" of this program.(111) Nevertheless, the apprehension about variables like socioeconomics remains. Hence the multitude of efforts to
shape a better reimbursement framework continues.
Eventually, greater reform in the reimbursement system is
necessary, but in the meantime, focusing on usability, minimizing computer time, and streamlining billing
documentation will be a welcome start.

The next prescription that needs to be written for our ailing
physicians, and for the health of the doctor-patient relationship, is instituting a more proactive burnout surveillance
program. Burnout is one of the most ruinous ramifications
of the fractured US healthcare system today. The less time
per patient due to insurance-controlled reimbursement, a
decrease in income, and the grinding quotidian logistical
hurdles in practice are causing an increased risk of burnout
for physicians. The hours spent in front of the EHR is yet another variable fueling this fire, which is why streamlining
EHR time and data entry is crucial.

Recall what I mentioned about how, in my experience, no
administrator or department head in a hospital or university *ever* asked me about how I was handling job stress as
an oncologist. During the coronavirus (SARS-CoV-2) pandemic of 2019-2020, there was a frightening burden
placed on doctors, nurses, and other healthcare workers

dealing with a serious illness on the front lines. I was quite curious about the degree to which doctors were being thrown into the fire, and so I spoke to dozens of my colleagues, asking them about the level of administrator support. We already touched on the concern that medical personnel were not able to speak up freely about the lack of protective equipment available in combating the SARS-CoV-2 virus.(101) Hence, I asked my colleagues a simple question: "Has anyone in the administration asked you personally how you are handling the stress of the coronavirus situation at your hospital?" Generic CEO emails to the entire medical staff or pithy social media posts did not count. The responses are revelatory. I received quick replies to my informal poll, with answers including "No, I feel abandoned," "They'd rather throw us under the bus," and "It depends on who you consider 'administration,' but the short answer is no." Note that these are colleagues of mine in different specialties who deal heavily with inpatient work, and would be highly exposed to potentially contracting SARS-CoV-2.

So how do we support doctors? The status quo is not acceptable. Over the years, I have seen many physicians—as well as a number of fantastic nurses—burn out, change jobs, and feel they could not continue and truly needed a break. Witnessing this, I am not completely surprised about the data regarding arguably the worst outcome stemming from burnout: physician suicide. According to research by the American Foundation for Suicide Prevention, male physicians commit suicide at a 70% higher rate compared with other professions, while female physicians die by their own hands at least 250% higher than women in other lines of work!(25) The AFSP cites key drivers of physician suicide to include "workload, work inefficiency, [and] lack of autonomy."

We need proactive burnout surveillance for early identification of those at risk of the consequences of burnout, including suicide. For any residents, medical students, and health policy or public health students reading this: this would be a tremendously valuable project for your research work. The traditional attitude of "toughing it out" is assuredly not the answer when it comes to burnout. A well-written article on this topic opined, "Healthcare systems have looked for easy fixes for physician distress, focusing on wellness (yoga, retreats, and self-care lessons), but this is misguided." The author of this article further wrote that this distress is "external to the physician and within the business framework of healthcare itself."(113) This viewpoint greatly resonates with me: yoga and new age "wellness retreats" are simply not going to address the underlying variables potentiating burnout! Rather, there needs to be a thoughtfully devised framework about recognizing signs and having the proper support and strategies to deal effectively with burnout. Otherwise, we would simply be accentuating the same factors that promote burnout in the first place.

Furthermore, in line with the same themes fracturing physicians and the doctor-patient relationship, burnout is becoming progressively worse. A survey of American physicians found that 78% of physicians had burnout, which reflected an increase of 4% since 2016. Equally alarming is that, in 2019, the British Medical Association revealed that 80% of doctors were at "high or very high risk of burnout."(114)

So who exactly should be navigating this ship scanning the waters for burnout risk? I feel the most logical options are either major professional societies or department heads at the physician's clinics. The latter—these department heads and administrators—have the advantage of understanding local issues but often have not been invested in this task, as evidenced from the experience of multiple colleagues of mine across the country. I offer kudos to those individual places where the department heads have truly been engaged in this vital effort, but unfortunately this is not the norm. Therefore, the former option, that of major professional societies, holds the promise of a uniform and widespread support network for doctors. This conceivably includes the AMA, as well as individual subspecialty societies, such as the American Society of Clinical Oncology.

For example, a major society such as the AMA may be able to staff a coordinated effort to detect burnout and those at risk of burning out. Interestingly, one approach may be to use one of the variables contributing to the current problem: mining data from EHRs. One study proposed multiple measurements to shed light on practice stress, including total EHR time, time on documentation, and time on prescriptions.(115) In other words, the total time spent clicking away at the computer rather than talking to patients may be an informative marker signaling burnout. For instance, it could be a screening tool to find those physicians who can benefit from further questioning; this can perhaps be the set of individuals spending three hours or more per day.

Others have advocated for informatics-based approaches to diminish burnout. In radiology, which is a highly technology-driven field, published research has suggested that "computer modifications to existing technology hold the potential to reduce the amount of time radiologists spend on noninterpretive tasks, decrease interruptions, facilitate connections with colleagues, and improve patient care."(116) While radiologists are not directly involved in the doctor-patient relationship in the mode of the family practice physician, such approaches could still successfully translate to multiple medical disciplines.

However, EHR time does not cover the full scope of the problem. Those clinicians who endured the marked stress from the SARS-CoV-2 pandemic can attest to that. Therefore, a more comprehensive questionnaire should be deployed to locate where someone falls on the burnout spectrum. One candidate for this is using a validated scale such as the Oldenburg Burnout Inventory (OLBI). (117, 118) In this particular scale, sixteen questions are posed to the subject, and respondents answer with a score of 1 to 4 (strongly agree, agree, disagree, and strongly disagree). In addition to having validation from the research arena, the questions make intuitive sense as well. Other well-established burnout tools have been published in the scientific literature also, such as the Maslach Burnout Inventory.(119) (See Table 2 for the specific questions in the OLBI scale.)

Oldenburg Burnout Inventory					
	Question				
1	I always find new and interesting aspects in my work.	1	2	3	4
2	There are days when I feel tired before I arrive at work.	1	2	3	4
3	It happens more and more often that I talk about my work in a negative way.	1	2	3	4
4	After work, I tend to need more time than in the past in order to relax and feel better.	1	2	3	4
5	I can tolerate the pressure of my work very well.	1	2	3	4
6	Lately, I tend to think less at work and do my job almost mechanically.	1	2	3	4
7	I find my work to be a positive challenge.	1	2	3	4
8	During my work, I often feel emotionally drained.	1	2	3	4
9	Over time, one can become disconnected from this type of work.	1	2	3	4
10	After working, I have enough energy for my leisure activities.	1	2	3	4
11	Sometimes I feel sickened by my work tasks.	1	2	3	4
12	After my work, I usually feel worn out and weary.	1	2	3	4
13	This is the only type of work that I can imagine myself doing.	1	2	3	4
14	Usually, I can manage the amount of my work well.	1	2	3	4
15	I feel more and more engaged in my work.	1	2	3	4
16	When I work, I usually feel energized.	1	2	3	4

Table 2. Questions comprising the Oldenburg Burnout Inventory.(117)
The 16 questions are scored by the respondent on a scale of 1 to 4 (1=Strongly Agree, 2=Agree, 3=Disagree, and 4=Strongly Disagree).

Thus, a proactive burnout surveillance program is desperately needed. Physicians across the country are either running a high risk of burning out or have already burned out. When doctors are enduring professional burnout, it weakens qualities that are part of the bedrock of a doctor's ethos: dedication and empathy. EHRs and overall computer time are strong variables sliding doctors toward burnout. As a publication examining burnout noted, "The highly trained U.S. physician . . . has become a data-entry clerk, required to document not only diagnoses, physician orders, and patient visit notes but also an increasing amount of low-value administrative data." (120, 121)

In my view, this is an immense opportunity for a physician-advocacy organization such as the AMA to generate positive change by coordinating a structured program to assess for burnout. Such a program can identify those in need and then direct those individuals to resources that can stabilize their professional crisis. An approach that may be fruitful is to screen practicing physicians with the very tool that is one of the factors accounting for the problem itself: electronic medical record systems. For those who spend at least three hours per day, for instance, they can then have that subset complete the relatively short 16-question Oldenburg Burnout Inventory (OLBI) questionnaire. Those who land on the concerning end of the OLBI scale can then be directed to engage with the resources that can help them, such as trained psychologists and other career counseling professionals. Akin to our seven types of doctors, this is a situation where the physician needs help. Feeling "abandoned" in the midst of extreme stress, as one of my colleagues told me during the SARS-CoV-2 pandemic, is not acceptable. The doctors are those members of society who have the most education and specialized medical training to help all of us—the general public. Do we expect firemen in poor health to save citizens in burning buildings? For these reasons, physician burnout requires effective mitigation, for the sake of us all.

The last major item on my list to heal the heart of medicine—that is, the practice of doctors and the doctor-patient relationship—is to reemphasize the indispensable value of rigorous medical education, particularly in training programs. We want the best and brightest physicians managing our health, and it is essential that training programs across the United States maintain a strident focus on education. Everyone realizes that, in today's healthcare schema, patient visits, treatments, and procedures bring in the money. However, regardless of that, I truly believe that as a medical community, it is our responsibility to prioritize clinical instruction and scientific thoroughness in medical education, thus imparting the best framework of knowledge for the next generation. Ultimately that means that twenty years from now, the generation of doctors treating all of us will have the proverbial "right stuff."

Recall how education is being diminished in today's training environment. With the dynamics we have discussed of ever-growing corporate-style clinics built on maximizing business objectives, clinical work is the de facto priority. There is no money in drawing time away from seeing patients and instead educating trainees. In discussions with multiple program directors and professors, all too often, education initiatives realistically can only be carried out through the sheer will of these teachers.

The consequences of the diminished importance of education in medical training are quite disconcerting. In an examination of training challenges in my own field of hematology, a spate of deficiencies were noted by authors from Imperial College London.(122) Firstly, the authors found a clear loss of laboratory hematology skills in new graduating trainees. This is significant in the field of hematology, where in-depth interpretation of laboratory studies is frequently required for proper diagnosis and treatment. They wrote, "Clinical hematologists need to maintain the basic skills in coagulation, blood transfusion and morphology that they have acquired during training, for the benefit both of their patients and their trainees." Related to this is proficiency in one of the core laboratory techniques: usage of the microscope to aid in medical diagnosis. The authors noted, "Cumulative microscopy exposure time has suffered a significant reduction," resulting in a lessened adeptness with the microscope.

Furthermore, this deficiency in lab science time flows into a larger problem. As the authors noted, "Previously hematologists functioned with a good understanding of laboratory techniques in addition to their clinical experience ... the supply of such multi-skilled hematologists may become part of the past."(122) Now as a clinical hematologist/oncologist, this is highly disturbing. Other investigations into imperfections of medical training have remarked similarly. In an article published in the medical literature, entitled "American medical education at a crossroads," the authors mentioned concerns, including a reduced ability to best translate scientific advances into real-world patient care and also that there are fewer graduates who will be true physician-scientists leading the research arena.(123)

So how can we rebalance the values of clinical work and education time in training hospitals? For one, the push for education has to come from the highest posts leading the training program. The voice of these individuals, who already believe in the necessity of a deep fund of medical knowledge, have to be heard, loud and clear. An intriguing solution that has been proposed is to teach interns *how to teach*. There have been pilot workshops conducted centered around "interns-as-teachers." By proactively learning skills to identify those quintessential teachable moments, these interns were able to better communicate nuances of a patient's management, for example, with greater clarity and also more effectively.(124) This approach also has the natural advantage of avoiding embarrassment; no one wants to convey an appearance of having insufficient knowledge in front of your colleagues and medical students. Anyone who has been in an office group meeting or conference call can relate to this feeling.

Medical education has the opportunity to modernize from another perspective as well: having students and trainees work with more physicians in outpatient clinical practice. I think of this as the reality check part of the intern's curriculum. Helping manage patients directly alongside practicing clinicians, rather than predominantly those in academic posts, allows the trainee to see the obstacles of real-world medicine. The doctor-in-training will thereby more innately grasp considerations such as cost. If we—the physician community—want to help push medicine toward lower costs, then where we refer patients matters. The student has to understand this from very early in their education to instill a cost-sensitive mindset. Another possible outcome of working with clinicians in practice is that those interns who are politically inclined may get motivated to engage with lawmakers to effect change at a policy level as well. There are too few of those currently, as reflected by the fact that only two senators in the 111th United States Congress (in 2020) were physicians. In contrast (and not surprisingly), there were 57 senators holding a law degree in that same Senate.(125)

Therefore medical education cannot be relegated to the back burner. An ardent emphasis on prioritizing education is vital for the future of the quality of physicians in America. We need training program directors pushing harder than ever on dedicating sufficient time toward the thorough learning of the scientific underpinnings of patient care. Examinations of training program deficiencies have already found highly concerning findings, such that some current graduates are short on vital proficiencies. One study referenced was conducted by doctors at the Imperial College London, whose motto is worth mentioning: "Scientia imperii decus et tutamen," which translates to "Scientific knowledge, the crowning glory and the safeguard of the empire."(126) In this vein, let us learn from the wisdom of the past and augment education for the sake of high-quality medical expertise to safeguard the health of us all.

Thus, we've discussed five major proposals as part of my "prescription" to effect positive change. These include proper regulation of health systems in local markets to galvanize cost-effective options, driving toward innovative physician reimbursement models to lessen dependency on health insurance, substantially streamline data entry so doctors can focus more time with patients, proactive surveillance for professional burnout, and elevating the place of medical education in training programs. (See Table 3.)

Prescription for Positive Change	
1	Price Transparency & Corporate Regulation
2	Innovative Payment Models away from Health Insurance
3	Streamline EHR Computer Software
4	Proactive Burnout Surveillance
5	Prioritize Medical Education

Table 3. *Five major proposals to "heal" medical practice in the United States.*

For the sake of the future of high-quality medical care and the health of the doctor-patient relationship, we have to rehabilitate the stresses that are currently pushing doctors to maladapt to the system. While there are other areas to rectify also, I feel these are the crucial ones that will get medical practice back on a better course. Our fictional Dr. Osler would not need to endure such pressure to fight health insurance decisions; Dr. Phillips would perceive a lesser need to give cosmetic treatments and consequently commit more time to pressing medical problems; Dr. Herbert would receive professional guidance rather than burning out. Hence, if these proposals were enacted, our seven types of doctors and the thousands of real clinicians they represent would be greatly helped.

15

REFLECTIONS

I am sitting back in my office chair again, gazing at the early morning sky, and contemplating. We've been around the ward of our seven doctors who are suffering from the calamitous stresses of the current healthcare system. What I have seen greatly disturbs me, particularly when I personally know a number of practicing doctors who have been affected by these very forces. Friends who have suffered burnout, those who have changed jobs due to frustration and professional dissatisfaction, and others who have left clinical medicine for nontraditional career options.

When I started my journey of exploring exactly how and why many of my colleagues have changed, I had to purposely pause and carefully think; only then was I struck by the profound craziness of how the American healthcare system has affected medical practice. And that's part of the reason we have come to this point in the medical field: in the relentless frenzy of medicine, there is no off-season to reevaluate and reconfigure. Instead, doctors are so fixated on the daily minutiae of patient care that too few take on the mantle of promoting change on a system level. Not surprisingly, political and policy engagement stereotypically does not animate most doctors. Ironically a favorite proverb among physicians that is applied to diagnosing a patient's condition is "Remember to see the forest for the trees." It is time to heed this proverb well for the sake of our profession and our patients.

The American public needs to hear and understand what is happening behind the medical office visit. For beyond the "check in", talking to the physician for 10 minutes, and then scheduling your next appointment, powerful currents are attacking the very heart of medicine: the doctor-patient relationship. Physicians are suffering frustration and burnout, fighting insurance companies to get the right medications for patients, and clicking away for hours *every day* on their computers. By the way, the insurance-driven 5- to 10-minute office visit is *not* the path of good medicine. One marker for the professional dissatisfaction is job turnover. Approximately 30% of doctors switch to a new job every three years.(99) Would this be happening—in any profession—if the situation was rosy? Definitely not; at one time, a doctor would proudly stay in the same practice for 20 to 30 years and deeply know their patients and community.

This is why I view the seven types of doctors as being patients themselves. They have been forced to make maladaptive changes due to the fissiparous stresses on the healthcare system. This is part of the fundamental reason doctors have not been able to, and cannot, fix these problems on their own. After all, we don't ask patients to treat themselves. Rather, we need solutions from the greater public in addition to physicians, thereby drawing from a more diverse skillset. This will better position us to drive positive change. Giving Joe and Jane Public a genuine voice is central to this, rather than to hyperactive lobby groups representing corporate interests, as the health of every *person* is at stake—not business entities!

In attempting to heal the integrity of the doctor-patient relationship, I have proposed five points that I feel, from my research and experience, will move us in the right direction. These points are naturally not meant to encompass a grand solution, but they address variables that need to be recuperated to staunch the bleeding—that is, minimize the fracturing of doctors into maladaptive styles of practice. Physicians departing in frustration to work at a new clinic every three years and spending literally hours a day in front of a computer rather than with patients is outrageously incompatible with what is best for patients. Even the doctor who finds greener pastures by leaving clinical medicine for options like pharmaceutical research or consulting, while successfully helping themselves escape the cavalcade of systemic problems, results ultimately in a loss for the countless patients who could have benefited from the doctor's expertise. It is quintessentially a brain drain from the perspective of patients, and this is why the emergence of these seven types of doctors reflects a problem impacting us all.

My suggestions include doctors switching to innovative payment models such as direct primary care, as well as strikingly streamlining the time and data entry tasks of EHR systems and proactively assessing for risk of burnout so physicians can obtain salubrious professional guidance when needed. These proposals that I have presented have gained some traction in the field—and therefore, if cohesively developed and expanded, could realistically foster a positive impact. For instance, I feel the direct primary care model holds much promise in delivering the type of medical care that is in the best interests of patients.

This has been an introspective journey for me, as I have examined the effects of a broken system on the behaviors of doctors. As I have seen these maladaptations in some of my friends and colleagues, this is particularly meaningful. I truly worry about the future of quality healthcare in the United States. Historically, many of the best and brightest students have answered the noble calling of medicine. However, if the trends discussed continue, I feel strongly that this will no longer hold true. And if that comes to pass, is it not a profound loss for us all?

Without a serious course correction for the medical profession, the next generation of doctors will not be able to practice the best medicine. Consequently, it is the health of all citizens that is suffering. Consider the study previously discussed about the deficiencies in the training of new graduates in hematology. Due to a sizeable fraction of new trainees not having the same level of proficiency in key areas compared to prior generations, the hematologist who is adept at melding subspecialized laboratory analysis with clinical management "may become part of the past."(122) Thus, if the best scientific minds are not entering medicine, and teaching has also eroded, then that is a recipe for reduced quality of future medical practice.

As I reflect on the implications of the maladaptations of physicians and the future of clinical practice, I also think of my own children. Unless my children absolutely love medicine (and I mean really, *really* love it), I am surely going to counsel them to go instead into finance, law, or an entrepreneurial profession. For the general public, this is a litmus test, no? If physician parents are recommending that their own children go into a field other than medicine, that is enormously telling.

EPILOGUE

C onsider this book an X-ray of the fractured system. Unfortunately, healing this fracture isn't as simple as setting a bone. Our seven types of doctors that we have explored reflect the experience of countless real clinicians across the United States, and the changes they have been compelled to make as a reaction to the severe stresses of the modern medical system. The classic axiom in medicine is primum non nocere, or first, do no harm. Tragically, the care of patients is indeed being harmed on account of the system and these changes.

There is still hope, however. We need to emphatically implement innovative solutions, and thereby make a dramatic course correction to set the healthcare system back on a path that strengthens the heart of medicine: the doctor-patient relationship. The question to all Americans is conceptually simple: do we want the brightest, most dedicated individuals to continue to go to medical school and then provide all patients with the best, compassionate evidence-based medical care? If so, then novel solutions are needed urgently.

I also want to reiterate that I am not at all aiming to criticize my colleagues. Rather, I am highly concerned about what is happening to doctors, such that doctors are forced to shift gears in a maladaptive way. Innumerable doctors have had to relocate away from traditional clinical medicine. That this ultimately damages the doctor-patient relationship, and thereby the health of the public, is a scathing insult to the ethos of good medical practice.

These negative forces and their effects on doctors remind me of one of my most challenging cases. In the mid-2000s, I was called to consult on a case for a 28-year-old lady who had developed severe anemia, or decreased red blood cell concentration. Her measurement was down over 50% when I first met her and fell to as low as approximately 75% below normal, which is life-threatening. During her clinical course, her liver started to fail, and she was in a very precarious position, where one bad turn could mean death. Furthermore, she developed difficulty with blood clotting from the liver failure, so she could bleed very easily. Multiple subspecialists in addition to myself were providing daily input, and I even remember an impromptu conference that five of us, from different fields in medicine, had in a corner of the intensive care unit. The fundamental reason for this proverbial meeting of the minds was simple: this was a human being who is dying, and we had to work as hard as possible—combined with hopefully drawing upon the right knowledge—to save this young patient.

In addition, we spent hours scouring the medical literature, endeavoring to piece together the elements of the case before it was too late. I even called a specialty laboratory in Utah late in the evening, to ensure a specimen was received by them, and implored them to run the analysis as fast as possible. And one of my fondest memories from this demanding case was when the senior hematologist and I *personally* wheeled the patient from a needed procedure all the way back to her room. While we were moving her through the hallways of the hospital, my senior colleague himself was spraying a medicine over the incision site on the skin to stop any excess bleeding. Trust me: you do not see this level of concern nowadays.

Eventually, as a result of this cumulative effort, we realized the patient had acute hemolytic crisis (red blood cell destruction) due to a rare genetic condition known as Wilson's Disease. In this condition, copper accumulates in the blood stream and liver, leading to liver failure and death without treatment. Fortunately for my patient, she was able to initiate the treatment to remove the copper from her body and then underwent a liver transplant successfully. She was cured; we were greatly relieved. We published our experience in the *Annals of Hematology* in 2009 for future clinicians to have in hand for their patients.(127)

I bring up this patient's case for the reader to reinforce a few points germane to our maladapting doctors. This patient would not have been saved without the collective dedication of multiple subspecialists. I was fortunate that my colleagues were some of the most intelligent doctors I know. They had the requisite dedication to go above and beyond any scheduled "shift" or work hours. Some of us were even discussing possibilities by phone at 10 o'clock at night. The patient came first, and we cared for our patient. I cannot state strongly enough that the multiple headwinds in the current healthcare system are changing all of this. If this same case presented to us today—with the current system and its problems—I truly wonder if we would have had the right colleagues, knowledge base, and dedication in place to save this same patient.

To paraphrase one of Socrates's great sayings, "The first step to wisdom is understanding what you do not know." Or rather, where are the important deficiencies? And where are the feasible opportunities to mitigate these problems? In our journey exploring the seven types of doctors, my goal was to illuminate these issues, as there is an inextricable link of how physicians practice medicine and the quality of healthcare patients receive. I firmly believe it is crucial for us to hold up a mirror to see the symptoms of the problems affecting the medical profession. Only by this introspection can we realistically stimulate the development of effective, timely solutions. Hopefully we are brave enough to look into that mirror and take action before it is too late, for the health of all Americans.

REFERENCES

1. American Medical Group Association News. Retention initiatives rise as physician turnover concerns increase. American Medical Group Association, 1422 Duke Street, Alexandria, VA, 22314, 14 March 2006.

2. "Centers for Medicare & Medicaid Services: Historical", Accessed June 6, 2018: https://www.cms.gov/Research-Statistics-Data-and-Systems/Statistics-Trends-and-Reports/NationalHealthExpendData/NationalHealthAccountsHistorical.html

3. "ICER Report: Costs of Approved CAR T-Cell Therapies Aligned With Clinical Benefit ", accessed June 6, 2018: http://www.ajmc.com/newsroom/icer-report-costs-of-approved-car-tcell-therapies-aligned-with-clinical-benefit

4. "Botulinum Toxin Market Size, Share & Regional Report", accessed June 6, 2018: https://www.fortunebusinessinsights.com/industry-reports/botulinum-toxin-market-100996

5. "Doctors blast ethics of $100,000 cancer drugs", accessed June 6, 2018: http://money.cnn.com/2013/04/25/news/economy/cancer-drug-cost/index.html

6. "Hospitals Acquired 5K Independent Practices from 2015 to 2016", accessed June 10, 2018: https://revcycleintelligence.com/news/hospitals-acquired-5k-independent-practices-from-2015-to-2016

7. "Physician Employment by Hospitals Increased Medicare Costs for Four Services by $3.1 Billion from 2012-2015", accessed June 10, 2018: http://www.physiciansadvocacyinstitute.org/Portals/0/assets/docs/PAI_PressRelease_110917.pdf

8. "High-Deductible Plans More Common, but So Are Choices", accessed June 14, 2018: https://www.shrm.org/resourcesandtools/hr-topics/benefits/pages/high-deductible-plans-more-common-but-so-are-choices.aspx

9. "National Vital Statistics Reports - Deaths: Final Data for 2015", accessed June 14, 2018: https://www.cdc.gov/nchs/data/nvsr/nvsr66/nvsr66_06.pdf

10. "Financial Toxicity and Cancer Treatment (PDQ) – Health Professional Version", accessed June 14, 2018: https://www.cancer.gov/about-cancer/managing-care/track-care-costs/financial-toxicity-hp-pdq

11. Bernard DS, Farr SL, Fang Z. National estimates of out-of-pocket health care expenditure burdens among nonelderly adults with cancer: 2001 to 2008. J Clinical Oncology. 2011 Jul 10;29(20): 2821-6.

12. "Prices soar as hospitals dominate cancer market", Accessed 11/3/2018. http://www.charlotteobserver.com/news/special-reports/prognosis-profits/article9083777.html

13. "What Is Insurance?", Accessed 11/3/2018. https://www.investopedia.com/terms/i/insurance.asp

14. "BCBS parent company posts $1.3B profit in 2017: 4 things to know", Accessed 11/3/2018. https://www.beckershospitalreview.com/payer-issues/bcbs-parent-company-posts-1-3b-profit-in-2017-4-things-to-know.html

15. "Health Insurance: Premiums and Increases", Accessed 11/3/2018. http://www.ncsl.org/research/health/health-insurance-premiums.aspx

16. "Health Insurance Coverage in the United States: 2016", Accessed 11/20/2018. https://www.census.gov/library/publications/2017/demo/p60-260.html

17. "Third-Quarter-2017-Profit-Margins", Accessed 11/20/2018. https://www.markfarrah.com/pressroom/Third-Quarter-2017-Profit-Margins-for-Leading-Blue-Cross-Blue-Shield-Plans.aspx

18. "Images Aren't Everything." *The Economist* Jun. 9 2018. Print.

19. Baker K, Sen S. Healing medicine's future: prioritizing physician trainee mental health. AMA J Ethics. 2016; 18(6): 604-613.

20. Tai-Seale M, Olson CW, Li J, Chan AS, Morikawa C et al. Electronic Health Record Logs Indicate That Physicians Split Time Evenly Between Seeing Patients And Desktop Medicine. Health Affairs. 2017; 36(4).

21. Khairat S, Burke G, Archambault H, Schwartz T, Larson J, Ratwani RM. Perceived Burden of EHRs on Physicians at Different Stages of Their Career. Appl Clin Inform. 2018 Apr;9(2):336-347.

22. Health reform and the decline of physician private practice. The Physicians Foundation. October 2010.

23. "The road less traveled: Non-traditional careers for physicians.", accessed July 1, 2016: https://wire.ama-assn.org/education/road-less-traveled-non-traditional-careers-physicians

24. "'I've Had It With Medicine!' 16 Options for Second Careers.", accessed August 20, 2018: https://www.medscape.com/viewarticle/827680

25. "Healthcare professional burnout, depression and suicide prevention", Accessed 11/20/2018. https://afsp.org/our-work/education/healthcare-professional-burnout-depression-suicide-prevention/#section1

26. "Physician Suicide and Support: Identify At-Risk Physicians and Facilitate Access to Appropriate Care", accessed 11/20/2018. https://www.stepsforward.org/modules/preventing-physician-suicide

27. Flexner A. Medical education in the United States and Canada: a report to the Carnegie Foundation for the Advancement of Teaching. New York: Carnegie Foundation for the Advancement of Teaching, 1910.

28. "What motivates us at work? More than money", accessed 11/25/2018. https://ideas.ted.com/what-motivates-us-at-work-7-fascinating-studies-that-give-insights/

29. "Workers are Losing Their Chains", The Economist, September 22, 2018

30. "Press Ganey Surveys", accessed 12/1/2018. http://www.pressganey.com/solutions/service-a-to-z/hcahps-regulatory-survey

31. "Acute Care Patient Experience Survey: What influences patients' ratings of their hospital?", accessed 12/1/2018. https://hqc.sk.ca/Portals/0/documents/factors-influencing-patient-hospital-experiences.pdf

32. "2+2=7? Seven things you may not know about Press Ganey Statistics", accessed 12/1/2018. http://epmonthly.com/article/227-seven-things-you-may-not-know-about-press-gainey-statistics/

33. "Are patient satisfaction surveys doing more harm than good?", Accessed 2/28/2019. https://www.beckershospitalreview.com/quality/are-patient-satisfaction-surveys-doing-more-harm-than-good.html

34. Fenton JJ, Jerant AF, Bertakis KD, Franks P. The cost of satisfaction: a national study of patient satisfaction, health care utilization, expenditures, and mortality. Arch Intern Med. 2012 Mar 12;172(5):405-11.

35. "Physician workload survey 2018", accessed 2/28/2019. https://locumstory.com/spotlight/physician-workload-survey-2018/

36. "Medscape Physician Lifestyle & Happiness Report 2018", accessed 2/28/19. https://www.medscape.com/slideshow/2018-lifestyle-happiness-6009320

37. Chen PGC, Curry LA, Bernheim SM, Berg D, Gozu A, Nunez-Smith M. Professional Challenges of Non-U.S.-Born International Medical Graduates and Recommendations for Support During Residency Training. Acad Med. 2011 Nov; 86(11): 1383–1388.

38. "Canada at a Glance 2018: Population", accessed 3/4/2019. https://www150.statcan.gc.ca/n1/pub/12-581-x/2018000/pop-eng.htm

39. "U.S. and World Population Clock", accessed 3/4/2019. https://www.census.gov/popclock/

40. "The Best Health Care System in the World: Which One Would You Pick?" *The New York Times* September 18, 2017. https://www.nytimes.com/interactive/2017/09/18/upshot/best-health-care-system-country-bracket.html

41. "Canada GDP", accessed 3/4/2019. https://tradingeconomics.com/canada/gdp

42. John C. Maxwell. *The 5 Levels of Leadership* (New York: Center Street, 2011).

43. Center for Workforce Studies. 2013 State Physician Workforce Data Book. Washington, DC: American Association of Medical Colleges; 2013.

44. Dill MJ, Slasberg ES; Center for Workforce Studies. The Complexities of Physician Supply and Demand: Projections Through 2025. Washington, DC; Association of American Medical Colleges; 2008.

45. Educational Commission for Foreign Medical Graduates (ECFMG). 2013 Annual Report. Philadelphia, PA: ECGMG; 2014.

46. National Resident Matching Program (NRMP). Results and Data: 2014 Main Residency Match. Washington, DC: NRMP; 2014.

47. "Waiting Your Turn: Wait Times for Health Care in Canada, 2017 Report", Accessed November 2, 2018: https://www.fraserinstitute.org/studies/waiting-your-turn-wait-times-for-health-care-in-canada-2017

48. "Wait Times in Canada - A Comparison by Province", accessed November 2, 2018: https://secure.cihi.ca/estore/productSeries.htm?pc=PCC395

49. "Office for National Statistics: Population Estimates", accessed 2/12/2019: https://www.ons.gov.uk/peoplepopulationandcommunity/populationandmigration/populationestimates

50. "International Health Care System Profiles: The English Health Care System", accessed 2/12/2019: https://international.commonwealthfund.org/countries/england

51. LaingBuisson, Health Cover UK Market Report, 12th ed., Aug. 2015, accessed 11/8/2018: http://www.laing-buisson.com/wp-content/uploads/2016/06/Health_Cover_12ed_Bro_WEB.pdf

52. "Changes to NICE drug appraisals: what you need to know", accessed 2/12/2019: https://www.nice.org.uk/news/feature/changes-to-nice-drug-appraisals-what-you-need-to-know

53. "Consumer Expenditures 2017", accessed 2/12/2019: https://www.bls.gov/news.release/cesan.nr0.htm

54. "Merck's Alimentary & Metabolism Drug Sales Have Likely Peaked" *Forbes* June 27 2018. Accessed 11/15/2018. https://www.forbes.com/sites/greatspeculations/2018/06/27/mercks-alimentary-metabolism-drug-sales-have-likely-peaked/

55. "FiercePharma: Lantus", accessed 11/15/2018: https://www.fiercepharma.com/special-report/1-lantus

56. "U.S. Unemployment Rate Drops To 3.7 Percent, Lowest In Nearly 50 Years", accessed 2/20/2019. https://www.npr.org/2018/10/05/654417887/u-s-unemployment-rate-drops-to-3-7-percent-lowest-in-nearly-50-years

57. "US Physician Job Demand Grows Again in 2018", accessed 2/20/2019. https://www.mdmag.com/medical-news/physician-job-demand-grows-again-in-2018

58. "Occupational Outlook Handbook: Physicians and Surgeons", accessed 2/20/2019. https://www.bls.gov/ooh/healthcare/physicians-and-surgeons.htm

59. "Where the revolving door is swiftest", accessed 2/20/2019. https://www.marketwatch.com/story/job-turnover-highest-in-nursing-child-care-retail

60. "Employees most likely to quit for a higher salary elsewhere", accessed 2/20/2019.
https://www.hrdive.com/news/employees-most-likely-to-quit-for-a-higher-salary-elsewhere/527382/

61. Adam Kay. *This is Going to Hurt* (London: Picador, 2017).

62. "Allergan Reports Fourth Quarter and Full-Year 2018 Financial Results", accessed 7/27/2019.
https://www.allergan.com/investors/news/thomson-reuters/allergan-reports-fourth-quarter-and-full-year-2018.aspx

63. "Testosterone Replacement Therapy Market Size Set to Register USD 1410 million by 2024", accessed 7/27/2019.
https://www.marketwatch.com/press-release/testosterone-replacement-therapy-market-size-set-to-register-usd-1410-million-by-2024-2019-04-09

64. "Global Cosmetic Products Market Will Reach USD 863 Billion by 2024: Zion Market Research", accessed 7/31/2019.
https://www.globenewswire.com/news-release/2018/06/22/1528369/0/en/Global-Cosmetic-Products-Market-Will-Reach-USD-863-Billion-by-2024-Zion-Market-Research.html

65. "Cosmetics Market size will Increase US$ 390 billion by 2024", accessed 7/31/2019. https://www.marketwatch.com/press-release/cosmetics-market-size-will-increase-us-390-billion-by-2024-2019-02-19

66. Poole KG. I want a doctor who looks like me: The dilemma of race-based requests. Cleveland Clinic Journal of Medicine. 2020; 87(5):268-269.

67. Raghu G, Weycker D, Edelsberg J, Bradford WZ, Oster G. Incidence and prevalence of idiopathic pulmonary fibrosis. Am J Respir Crit Care Med. 2006; 174(7):810.

68. "Study Shows First Job after Medical Residency Often Doesn't Last", Accessed 7/2/2019. https://www.prnews-wire.com/news-releases/study-shows-first-job-after-medical-residency-often-doesnt-last-161949055.html

69. "Treating Aging with Testosterone", accessed 8/7/19. https://www.aafp.org/afp/2017/1001/p428.html

70. "Treating low testosterone levels", accessed 8/7/19. https://www.health.harvard.edu/mens-health/treating-low-testosterone-levels

71. "CNN Profiles – Dr. Sanjay Gupta – Chief Medical Correspondent", accessed 8/14/19. https://www.cnn.com/profiles/sanjay-gupta-profile

72. Song Z. The Pricing of Care Under Medicare for All. JAMA. 2019;322(5):395-396.

73. "How do national health insurers compare on denying claims?", accessed 8/17/19. https://www.post-gazette.com/business/healthcare-business/2014/11/13/National-insurers-compete-for-foot-hold-in-Pittsburgh-market/stories/201411130178

74. "Medicare more likely to deny claims than commerical health insurers", accessed 8/17/19. https://www.healthcare-economist.com/2008/06/30/medicare-more-likely-to-deny-claims-than-commerical-health-insurers/

75. "If I Have a BRCA1 or BRCA2 Gene Mutation, Should I Get a Preemptive Mastectomy?", accessed 8/21/19. https://health.usnews.com/health-care/patient-advice/articles/2017-04-11/if-i-have-the-brca1-or-brca2-gene-should-i-get-a-preemptive-mastectomy

76. Schulman KA, Milstein A. The Implications of "Medicare for All" for US Hospitals. JAMA. 2019;321(17):1661-1662.

77. Joseph JW, Davis S, Wilker EH, Wong ML, Litvak O, Traub SJ et al. Modelling attending physician productivity in the emergency department: a multicentre study. Emerg Med J. 2018 May;35(5):317-322.

78. "Efficiency in the Emergency Department", accessed 10/17/19. https://www.acep.org/imports/clinical-and-practice-management/resources/administration/efficiency-in-the-emergency-department/

79. "Staffing Your Emergency Department Efficiently, Effectively, and Safely: Core Concepts", accessed 10/17/19. https://www.envisionphysicianservices.com/campaigns/breakthrough-series/presentation-materials/presentations/09-staffing-your-ed-core-concepts.pdf

80. Chen Z, Liu C, Huang J, Zeng P, Lin J, Zhu R et al. Clinical Efficacy of Extracorporeal Cardiopulmonary Resuscitation for Adults with Cardiac Arrest: Meta-Analysis with Trial Sequential Analysis. Biomed Res Int. 2019; 2019: 6414673.

81. Hariri S, Bozic KJ, Lavernia C, Prestipino A, and Rubash HE. Medicare Physician Reimbursement: Past, Present, and Future. J Bone Joint Surg Am. 2007; 89:2536-2546.

82. Moore MJ and Bennett CL. The Learning Curve for Laparoscopic Cholecystectomy. Am J Surg 1995; 170(1):55.

83. Hoballah JJ, Liao J, Salameh M, and Weigel R. Physician Reimbursement for General Surgical Procedures in the Last Century: 1906 – 2006. J Am Coll Surg. 2008.

84. Marder WD, Emmons DW, Kletke PR, Willke RJ. Physician employment patterns: challenging conventional wisdom. Health Aff (Millwood). 1988;7(5):137-145.

85. Mathews AW. When the doctor has a boss: more physicians are going to work for hospitals rather than hanging a shingle. Wall Street Journal. November 8, 2010.

86. Charles AG, Ortiz-Pujols S, Ricketts T, Fraher, E, Neuwahl S, Cairns B et al. The Employed Surgeon: A Changing Professional Paradigm. JAMA Surg. 2013;148(4):323-328.

87. Ball CG, MacLean AR, Kirkpatrick AW, et al. Hepatic vein injury during laparoscopic cholecystectomy: the unappreciated proximity of the middle hepatic vein to the gallbladder bed. J Gastrointest Surg 2006; 10:1151.

88. Strasberg SM, Hertl M, Soper NJ. An Analysis of the Problem of Biliary Injury during Laparoscopic Cholecystectomy. J Am Coll Surg. 1995; 180(1):101.

89. Jena AB, Seabury S, Lakdawalla D, Chandra A. Malpractice Risk According to Physician Specialty. N Engl J Med. 2011 Aug 18; 365(7): 629-636.

90. Gómez-Durán EL, Vizcaíno-Rakosnik M, Martin-Fumadó C, Klamburg J, Padrós-Selma J, Arimany-Manso J. Physicians as second victims after a malpractice claim: An important issue in need of attention. J Healthc Qual Res. 2018 Sep – Oct;33(5):284-289.

91. Paterick ZR, Patel N, Chandrasekaran K, Tajik J, Paterick TE. Medical Malpractice Stress Syndrome: A "Forme Fruste" of Posttraumatic Stress Disorder. J Med Pract Manage. 2017 Jan;32(4):283-287.

92. "AMA: Medical Professional Liability Insurance Premiums: An Overview of the Market from 2008 to 2017", Accessed 11/20/2019. https://www.ama-assn.org/sites/ama-assn.org/files/corp/media-browser/public/government/advocacy/policy-research-perspective-liability-insurance-premiums.pdf

93. "With the price capped for knee replacement, more people can avail it", Accessed 1/2/2020. https://economictimes.indiatimes.com/opinion/interviews/with-the-price-capped-for-knee-replacement-more-people-can-avail-it-vikram-shah-cmd-shalby-hospitals/articleshow/60101228.cms

94. "Understanding Knee Replacement Costs: What's on the Bill?", Accessed 1/2/2020. https://www.healthline.com/health/total-knee-replacement-surgery/understanding-costs

95. Williams A. Haseltine. *World Class: A Story of Adversity, Transformation, and Success at NYU Langone Health* (New York: Fast Company Press, 2019).

96. "Sunshine is a Partial Disinfectant." *The Economist* Nov. 23 2019. Print.

97. "340B Program May Hinder Access to Costly Drugs as Hospitals Exploit Discounts: CRE", Accessed 1/10/2020. https://www.fiercehealthcare.com/hospitals-health-systems/340b-hospitals-reducing-uninsured-access-to-quality-healthcare-cre

98. "Active Physicians with a U.S. Doctor of Medicine (U.S. MD) Degree by Specialty, 2015", accessed 2/23/2020. https://www.aamc.org/data-reports/workforce/interactive-data/active-physicians-us-doctor-medicine-us-md-degree-specialty-2015

99. Willard-Grace R, Knox M, Huang B, Hammer H, Kivlahan C, Grumbach K. Burnout and Health Care Workforce Turnover. Ann Fam Med. 2019 Jan;17(1):36-41.

100. Schwenk TL. What Does It Mean to Be a Physician? JAMA. 2020 Mar; 323(11): 1037-1038.

101. "Amid PPE Shortage, Clinicians Face Harassment, Firing for Self-Care", Accessed 4/8/2020. https://www.medscape.com/viewarticle/927590

102. "7 ways to reduce medical school debt", Accessed 5/17/2020. https://www.aamc.org/news-insights/7-ways-reduce-medical-school-debt

103. Wolfe ID and Pope TM. Hospital Mergers and Conscience-Based Objections – Growing Threats to Access and Quality of Care. N Engl J Med. 2020 Apr;382(15):1388-1389.

104. "Protecting Statutory Conscience Rights in Health Care; Delegations of Authority", Accessed 4/8/2020. https://www.federalregister.gov/documents/2019/05/21/2019-09667/protecting-statutory-conscience-rights-in-health-care-delegations-of-authority

105. "Direct Primary Care", Accessed 4/9/2020. https://www.aafp.org/about/policies/all/direct-primary.html

106. "The Doctor Will See You but Not Your Insurance", Accessed 4/9/2020. https://www.aarp.org/health/health-insurance/info-08-2013/direct-primary-care.html

107. "What is Direct Primary Care?", Accessed 4/9/2020. https://www.dpcare.org

108. "Medicare Provider Utilization and Payment Data: Physician and Other Supplier", Accessed 4/15/2020. https://www.cms.gov/Research-Statistics-Data-and-Systems/Statistics-Trends-and-Reports/Medicare-Provider-Charge-Data/Physician-and-Other-Supplier

109. Young RA, Holder S, Kale N, Burge SK, Kumar KA. Coding Family Medicine Residency Clinic Visits, 99213 or 99214? A Residency Research Network of Texas Study. Fam Med. 2019 Jun;51(6):477-483.

110. "CMS' Verma announces new meaningful measures initiative", Accessed 4/16/2020.
https://www.fiercehealthcare.com/practices/cms-seema-verma-announces-new-meaningful-measures-initiative

111. "A health care paradox: measuring and reporting quality has become a barrier to improving it", Accessed 4/16/2020.
https://www.statnews.com/2017/12/13/health-care-quality/

112. "Quality Measures Requirements", Accessed 4/19/2020.
https://qpp.cms.gov/mips/quality-

measures

113. "Why 'Burnout' Is the Wrong Term for Physician Suffering", Accessed 4/19/2020.
https://www.medscape.com/viewarticle/915097

114. Physician burnout: a global crisis. Lancet. 2019 Jul 13;394(10193):93.

115. Sinsky CA, Rule A, Cohen G, Arndt BG, Shanafelt TD, Sharp CD et al. Metrics for assessing physician activity using electronic health record log data. J Am Med Inform Assoc. 2020 Apr 1;27(4):639-643.

116. Simon AF, Holmes JH, Schwartz ES. Decreasing radiologist burnout through informatics-based solutions. Clin Imaging. 2020 Feb;59(2):167-171.

117. Demerouti E and Mostert K. Burnout and Work Engagement: A Thorough Investigation of the Independency of Both Constructs. Journal of Occupational Health Psychology. 2010, Vol. 15, No. 3, 209–222.

118. Reis D, Xanthopoulou D, Tsaousis I. Measuring job and academic burnout with the Oldenburg Burnout Inventory (OLBI): Factorial invariance across samples and countries. Burnout Research. 2015; 2(1):8-18.

119. C. Maslach, S.E. Jackson. The measurement of experienced burnout. Journal of Organizational Behavior. 1981;2(2):99-113.

120. Downing NL, Bates DW, Longhurst CA. Physician Burnout in the Electronic Health Record Era: Are We Ignoring the Real Cause? Ann Intern Med. 2018 Jul 3; 169(1):50-51.

121. Fred HL, Scheid MS. Physician Burnout: Causes, Consequences, and (?) Cures. Tex Heart Inst J. 2018 Aug 1;45(4):198-202.

122. Shlebak AA, Bain BJ. Training future haematologists, a privilege or a burden? "A trainer's view". Br J Haematol. 2017 Aug;178(4):501-507.

123. Feldman AM, Runge MS, Garcia JGN and Rubenstein AH. American medical education at a crossroads. Sci Transl Med. 2015 Apr 29;7(285).

124. Donovan AK, Linz DR, Rubio DM, McNeil MA, Spagnoletti CL. Teaching to Teach: An Effective and Feasible Teaching Curriculum for Internal Medicine Interns. South Med J. 2018 Dec;111(12):733-738.

125. "Members of the 111th United States Congress", Accessed 4/25/2020. https://en.wikipedia.org/wiki/Members_of_the_111th_United_States_Congress

126. "The College crest", Accessed 4/25/2020. https://www.imperial.ac.uk/about/history/the-college-crest/

127. Mehta AR, Salaru G, Harrison JS. Stomatocytosis heralding a case of acute Wilsonian crisis. Ann Hematol. 2010 May;89(5):527-9. Epub 2009 Sep 24.

128. Koven S. The Doctor's New Dilemma. N Engl J Med. 2016 Feb 18;374(7): 608-9.

129. Bolster L and Rourke L. The Effect of Restricting Residents' Duty Hours on Patient Safety, Resident Well-Being, and Resident Education: An Updated Systematic Review. J Grad Med Educ. 2015 Sep; 7(3): 349–363.

Made in United States
North Haven, CT
21 January 2023

31408968R00143